THE KESTREL

HAMLYN SPECIES GUIDES

THE KESTREL

Michael Shrubb

HAMLYN

COVER ILLUSTRATION: *Adult male Kestrel alert on a fence post.*

Published in 1993 by The Hamlyn Publishing
Group Limited (part of Reed Consumer Books),
Michelin House, 81 Fulham Road, London SW3 6RB

The photographs are copyright and are reproduced by permission of the following:
pp. 15, 94, 102 M. Hollings; pp. 30, 103 Kim Taylor/Bruce Coleman Ltd;
p. 47 Frank Greenaway/Bruce Coleman Ltd; p. 51 Konrad Wothe/Bruce
Coleman Ltd; pp. 83, 86, 95 Roger Tidman; p. 91 M. Shrubb.

British Library Cataloguing in Publication Data

Shrubb, Michael
  Kestrel. – Hamlyn Species Guides)
  I. Title II. Series
  598.9

ISBN 0-540-01278-5

Series Editor David A. Christie
Page design by Jessica Caws
Maps by Louise Griffiths
Printed in Hong Kong

CONTENTS

Scavenging and piracy, both regular habits of Kestrels. ABOVE *alert male eyeing hunting owl.* BELOW *adult female at dead Hare* (see page 60).

Series Editor's Foreword

IN most parts of Britain and the rest of Europe, the Kestrel is the one bird of prey that the majority of people are likely to see. It has entered our cities, where it can now be seen in even the most built-up areas, sometimes choosing to nest on the ledges of high-rise blocks. It is also a frequent sight as it hovers above road and motorway verges or perches on a bridge or fencepost along the route of the highway. Although we immediately think of a Kestrel as a bird that hovers (it is still known in some places by its old name of 'Windhover'), it may also be searching for prey when it is perched – what is known as 'still-hunting'.

Nevertheless, this is a bird that really belongs to the open countryside, and that is where it is seen at its best as it glides rapidly and effortlessly across an open field, hangs in the wind above a cliff-edge top or disappears into a small copse. Perhaps it is in farmland that the Kestrel is most at home, and it is in such a habitat that Michael Shrubb has done most of his studies on this fascinating little falcon, studies extending over several decades.

I like to watch young Kestrels in summer, when they have just left the nest and are learning to hunt for themselves. In Britain at least, this species is normally solitary, but at this time of the year it is possible to see five or six together as the parents accompany their young for a few weeks, the youngsters often sitting around on low perches while the adults show them what they must do if they are to survive for more than just a few months in the harsh world of nature (many young do not live beyond their first winter).

There are many intriguing aspects to the life of the Kestrel. Michael Shrubb, who knows these birds far better than most other ornithologists do, helps us to understand the significance of such matters as why the male and female have different plumages, why some individuals migrate while others seem to spend their whole life within one small area, the different hunting methods and when they are used, and so on. Having read this book, it is difficult to watch that falcon hovering beside the motorway without reflecting over all the hidden complexities in the life of this appealing bird of prey.

David Christie

Introduction and Acknowledgements

KESTRELS have long fascinated me. Any falcon that preys on items ranging from ladybirds to rats too large for it to lift, from bats to fish, or from Swallows to dragonflies must be worth attention. Their appeal is more subtle than the dramatic behaviour of creatures such as Peregrines, but kestrels are nevertheless impressive and often surprisingly formidable birds. They are also beautiful. For the raptor enthusiast, too, they combine the advantages of ubiquity and tolerance of humanity. There can be few places in Britain that are not graced by them at some season, to impress us with their dash and versatility and to provide, in their great variety of behaviour, an endless source of delight and study.

Altogether thirteen species have the name kestrel, derived from the Old French *Cresserelle* or *Cristel* (still used by the French as the common name) and said by Alfred Newton (1896) to refer to the tinkling nature of the call; this certainly seems to be the derivation of the scientific name *tinnunculus* of the Common Kestrel. All are small or small to medium-sized falcons. Three species are basically grey; in the remainder, red (actually shades of chestnut-pink to rufous-brown or russet) is a dominant colour. Although the grey species – Grey Kestrel*, Dickinson's Kestrel and Barred Kestrel – do not resemble typical kestrels at all in plumage, they undoubtedly do in certain physical characteristics and Cade (1982) classes them as aberrant kestrels in his organization of the genus *Falco*. Of the ten red or typical kestrels, two are island forms with very tiny populations. The remainder tend to be rather numerous and successful. Often their habits have enabled them to take great advantage of Man's modification of forested habitats. This book deals with one of the most successful and widespread species, found throughout Eurasia and much of Africa, *Falco tinnunculus*, in English known simply as the Kestrel or the Common Kestrel but in much of Europe known as the 'Tower Falcon', from its frequent habit of nesting in sites such as church towers. Much of the material is drawn from my own studies of the bird in coastal Sussex and upland Breconshire. In my Sussex study area, I examined breeding and winter density over an area of 38 km² of mixed and arable farmland, devoted to grass, cereals, peas, oil-seed rape and potatoes, and made more detailed studies of the behaviour of a small group of pairs on part of this area totalling *c*. 1500 ha and comprising my family's and five neighbouring farms. In upland Breconshire, my area comprises improved grassland, open hill grazings and forestry plantations, the grassland devoted very largely to intensive sheep-rearing.

I have drawn heavily from other studies, particularly that of Dr Andrew Village, who published a very detailed account of the species in 1990.

*Scientific names are given on page 125

8

The account of nesting is based largely on the nest record cards of the British Trust for Ornithology (BTO), while that of movements uses their ringing returns. The book does not pretend to be a definitive monograph. Much of the most detailed work on the Kestrel derives from a very limited part of its range, which may bias our understanding of it. I have also tried to complement Andrew Village s book rather than emulate it.

Acknowledgements

I have to thank the BTO for access to their nest record cards and ringing returns. These schemes are partly funded by a grant from the Joint Nature Conservation Committee (JNCC). I am also grateful to David Gibbons for a preview of the new *Atlas* results for Kestrels breeding in Britain and Ireland, and the BTO's Librarian, Philip Jackson, for his considerable help in tracking down and copying voluminous references for me. Dr Michael Hollings has supplied some of the photographs, and he and many other friends, particularly Roy Sandison and Stuart Hughes, have, over the years, discussed ideas about Kestrels with me and supplied me with information. I also have to thank my neighbours in Sussex and Wales for their tolerance of my wanderings over their land, Brian Langmead for access to his comprehensive library of early avifaunas. and finally my wife, not only for her forbearance during the throes of composition, but also for her considerable help in checking and correcting proofs.

Head of a male Kestrel. Note the rather large eye. Kestrels are often crepuscular.

1

THE KESTREL GROUP

THE typical kestrels form a fairly distinctive group within the genus *Falco*. Broadly, they are linked by certain plumage features, certain characteristics of build and proportions and by hunting behaviour. None of these characteristics is necessarily true of all (not all hover, for example), but most share sufficient to be obviously kestrels. Their combined distribution is worldwide.

Plumage

A basic distinction is simply that the reddish colour of the upperparts of typical kestrels is very uncommon as a dominant plumage feature in other falcons; the latter tend towards blues, greys or colder earth-browns (see colour plate 3, page 67). Secondly, the pattern of the upperparts of typical kestrels tends to show much greater contrasts than in other falcons; again, this is illustrated in colour (plate 3) for the falcons breeding regularly in Britain, and it appears to be true for most falcons. The sharp contrast of blackish outer wing and paler reddish-brown back and inner wing will often distinguish kestrels at considerable range. My own observations of Kestrel suggest that the strongly defined pattern of the upperparts is linked to territorial behaviour.

Typical kestrels are usually stated to be more sexually dimorphic in plumage (i.e., male and female differ in coloration) than other falcons, but this is marked only in Kestrel, American Kestrel, Lesser Kestrel and Australian Kestrel and, among other falcons, the Merlin and Red-footed and Eastern Red-footed Falcons show equally marked dimorphism. Nevertheless, the differences among kestrels in this respect are interesting. Village (1990) pointed out that plumage dimorphism was most marked in those typical kestrels whose ranges extend furthest north or south of the equator; these species also all include migratory populations. The six species of typical kestrel showing reduced or minimal dimorphism are also divided between those in which the male has feminine plumage (i.e., it increasingly resembles female Kestrel) and those in which the female has moved towards masculine plumage (with the reverse characteristics). Colour plate 1 opposite shows some of the variations involved. As Cade (1982) remarks, there is no obvious geographical or any other factor in these variations. For example, the two most restricted island species show almost complete divergence in opposite directions, the female Seychelles Kestrel having an

Plumages of some typical kestrel species compared, to show differing degrees of sexual dimorphism.

Lesser Kestrel
(male)

Lesser Kestrel
(female)

Common Kestrel
(female)

Common Kestrel
(male)

Greater Kestrel
(sexes similar)

Moluccan Kestrel
(male)

Moluccan Kestrel
(female)

Figure 1.1 *Tail length as a percentage of wing length in Kestrels and other falcons compared.*

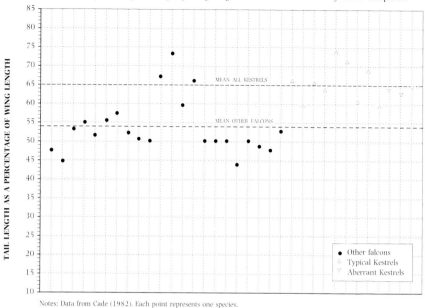

Notes: Data from Cade (1982). Each point represents one species.

Figure 1.2 *Wing-loading in Kestrels and other falcons compared.*

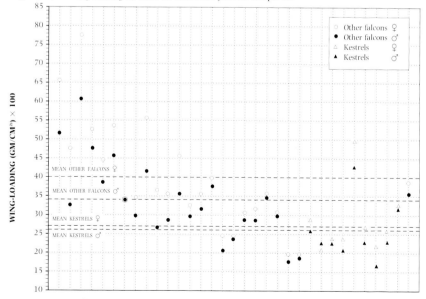

Note: Data from Cade (1982). Each pair of points represents one species.

Figure 1.3 *Wing-loading in falcons in relation to diet.*

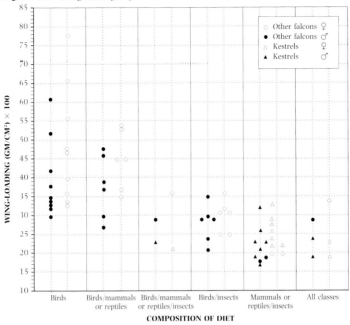

Data sources in text. Each point represents one species.

almost completely male plumage and the male Mauritius Kestrel a female plumage; both are tropical and are, or were, adapted to forest.

One point may be significant. All the markedly dimorphic kestrels hover-hunt, and the typical kestrels which are sedentary, not strikingly dimorphic but are stated to hover-hunt regularly (Moluccan, Madagascar and Greater Kestrels) all have grey tails contrasting with the upperparts. For the Kestrel, the grey tail of the male makes a very conspicuous signal and may, for example, help to separate hunting males when their hunting ranges overlap (page 61). Perhaps this is more general among all kestrels. The possible link between migratory habits and plumage dimorphism may also be significant, for something of the patterns and variations discussed here arises also in races of the Kestrel.

Build, proportions and hunting

All kestrels differ from other falcons in certain physical features. Their tails are longer in proportion to wing length (Figure 1.1). They also have lower wing-loadings, i.e., the area of the wing is greater in proportion to body weight (Figure 1.2). Kestrels therefore show important aerodynamic differences compared with most other falcons. These reflect diet and hunting behaviour. Figure 1.3 relates wing-loading to diet for those falcons for which some information on the former is available in Cade (1982).

Details of diet are drawn from Cade, Cramp and Simmons (1979) and Brown and Amadon (1968), and species are grouped according to their principal types of diet. Clearly, species feeding to an important extent on insects have lower wing-loadings than those feeding primarily on birds or mammals. Lower wing-loading provides more lift and, for kestrels which also hunt by hovering, the increased tail area adds to this. Other falcons need speed and weight to generate stopping power and hence have higher wing-loadings. Interestingly, when Kestrels attack birds, the flight surfaces are closed right up and the attack is launched either from a height or from a distance, similarly generating speed and stopping power (page 53).

Hover-hunting appears to be recorded for all except Fox and Seychelles Kestrels, but standard accounts are rather contradictory on how often some other species hover. For example, it seems probable that Mauritius, Grey and Barred Kestrels do so rarely, if at all. Hovering, however, is simply a form of perched hunting or still-hunting – using stationary flight to search areas beyond the range of fixed perches. All kestrels hunt from perches to a great extent and take much of their prey on the ground by stealth and surprise, another important difference from many other falcons.

Reversed size dimorphism

Among most birds the sexes differ in size (size dimorphism), males being the larger. In kestrels, as in all raptors, the female is larger. This reversed size dimorphism has caused much discussion. Its scale varies with diet, for example, sexes of raptors taking large and agile prey differing most in size (see Newton 1979). Newton used wing length to measure differences as the only statistic available for many species, although, as Cade (1982) has pointed out, differences in weight are often more marked. In the Kestrel, for example, the wing-length of males is about 96 per cent of that of females but males weigh only about 80 per cent as much as females. This results in a difference in wing-loading between the sexes, which apparently occurs in all falcons to some degree (Figure 1.2). Thus, they differ aerodynamically, and marked size dimorphism can result in dietary differences between the sexes (see Newton 1986 for Sparrowhawk). This may occur to some extent in less markedly dimorphic species, and I have observed it in Kestrel (page 46).

These interesting patterns do not, however, explain why females are the larger. This is related to the female's breeding role of storing large bodily reserves for laying and incubation (Newton 1986). It is clearly advantageous for females to have a larger airframe for storing these reserves.

Geographic distribution

Apart from Mauritius and Seychelles Kestrels, kestrels are not adapted to dense forest habitats; nor are they adapted to extreme desert, although they do occur in many arid habitats. Otherwise they have a wide geographical distribution, being found in all zoogeographical regions. Despite this cosmopolitan distribution there are interesting gaps. They have not colonized New Zealand, despite an ability to reach remote oceanic islands. More

Male (right) and female Kestrel at the nest. These photographs show clearly the difference in weight and build betwen the sexes, as well as those of plumage.

surprisingly, they are absent as breeding birds from much of peninsular India, south-east Asia and Sumatra, Borneo and the Philippines, although Kestrels winter there. In addition, Brown (1970) noted that they were scarce as breeding birds in apparently suitable grasslands in East Africa, although again wintering. Interestingly, the harriers, which feed on a similar range of prey from similar habitats, show very similar distributional gaps.

Common Kestrel

The Common Kestrel is the most widely distributed of the species, although it is probably less numerous than the American Kestrel (Cade 1982). Nevertheless, it is by far the most numerous Old World falcon. Of the size scale of a Jackdaw, the adult male is a beautiful bird with a blue-grey head, a pale face with slender dark 'moustache', a rufous back and inner wings – often quite pinkish in some lights – with dark spots, and a blue-grey rump and tail with black subterminal band. The outer upperwing is blackish and sharply defined from the rufous of the inner wing and back. The underparts are pale buffish with darker markings, the underwing being palest and only lightly marked; often it flashes very white in bright sun. The eye is dark and large (kestrels are often crepuscular) and the legs and cere are yellow. The females are less contrastingly patterned: the head is brown with darker streaks, and the back rufous-brown and more heavily marked, the blackish markings tending to form lateral bars; the tail is also brown and barred blackish, with a broader blackish subterminal band.

15

Females often show little moustachial, and the underparts and underwing are more heavily marked and darker than in males. Both sexes show a white edge along the extreme tip of the tail in fresh plumage, but it is lost or very inconspicuous in worn plumage. When the two sexes are seen together the greater size of females is usually fairly obvious, but males and females may overlap in size. To my eye, females are often distinctly colder in colour on the upperparts than males and the blackish outer wing is also less sharply defined.

Females often also show some grey at the base of the tail and rump and some have entirely greyish tails, although the tail is always barred and the grey colour milky in tinge rather than blue. The blue head of males can also be surprisingly difficult to distinguish in the field and their upperparts may show subtle colour variations, from a very rich dark chestnut to a decidedly 'washy' colour. Although sometimes tricks of the light, such variations mean that Kestrels can be surprisingly difficult to sex accurately in the field. Often I find the sharper colour contrasts of the male and the greater 'heft' of the female the best guides.

Juveniles are very neat and trim little birds in fresh plumage and their distinctively white-tipped tails are a good distinction from adults in their first weeks, when adult plumage is always abraded. They resemble females but they often appear distinctly warmer, more rufous, in general colour, again perhaps a function of bright, fresh plumage. Structurally they show distinctly more rounded wings than adults, a distinction lost as primaries wear. Many juveniles, particularly males, show a variable amount of grey in the tail from the first plumage. In males, the progression to fully adult plumage takes two to three years.

In flight, compared with most other falcons, kestrels look more delicately built and long-tailed and the normal flight is lighter. A kestrel in a hurry, however, looks very different, and it is particularly instructive to see one approaching fast head-on, when it appears altogether more strongly and heavily built and more purposeful. At rest they often adopt a 'hunched-shouldered' attitude and then look more sturdy than they do in flight.

Kestrels, like all raptors, will often be seen against the sky without any background or reference point to judge distance, size, colour or pattern. In such circumstances I have called them Peregrines, Hobbies, Merlins and Sparrowhawks, until observation showed otherwise. Many people think: 'kestrel – hovers', but the bird may be soaring at great height, displaying, stooping at something on the ground or beating up some hapless avian passer-by (harriers are particularly liable to provoke kestrels' wrath). In all such circumstances they will look quite different, usually because flight surfaces are closed right up, changing their shape radically; soaring birds expand theirs, however, hence the confusion at times with Sparrowhawks. Weather conditions, in particular strong winds, will also alter appearances, and any raptor should be watched carefully while it is in view for no group of birds has a greater aptitude for making a complete fool of the observer.

In Britain, however, there are no true confusion species; it is circumstances which may cause confusion. In parts of Europe, Kestrels must be separated from Lesser Kestrels and probably from juvenile Red-footed

Falcons. My experience of the last two is limited but, with clear views, there should be few problems in separating Lesser Kestrels. Males have a clear, bright, unspotted chestnut mantle and a pale grey or blue-grey head and tail. Unlike Kestrels they have no moustachial line and the blue extends over the cheeks, giving the bird a quite different facial expression resembling a Classical Greek helmet. Much of the inner upperwing is also blue-grey, but my notes suggest that this may not be as striking as illustrations suggest. The underwing is notably pale silvery and more or less unmarked except for a black tip to the primaries. Thus, the general pattern is brighter and cleaner than Kestrel's, and female Lesser Kestrels similarly have a much paler underwing, which I have found a good distinction from Common. Lesser Kestrels are also slighter and more elegant in build. They are generally colonial and gregarious (so may Kestrels be) and spend much time hawking flying insects, when the flight appears more positive and graceful than Kestrel's, more Hobby-like, but they also hover-hunt and occur singly and may often be difficult to separate.

Red-footed Falcons also hover-hunt, but adults should cause no confusion with Kestrels. Juveniles may: one I saw had upperparts not unlike a nearby female Kestrel, particularly when perched, when it adopted the same 'hunched-shouldered' posture, but it had much whitish about the head, which immediately distinguished it, and, in flight, it was strikingly Hobby-like in build and action. As so often with raptors, separating these species will often depend as much on a good knowledge of shape, build and flight attitudes as on plumage features. Such differences can be learned only by practice and experience.

2
RACES AND DISTRIBUTION

ELEVEN races of the Common Kestrel are recognized. Four are island forms in the Canary and Cape Verde archipelagos, four occur in Africa, one also breeding in Arabia, and three are found in much of Eurasia. Three are partly migratory, the remainder are sedentary so far as is known. Establishing such facts requires careful comparisons of series of individuals from different areas, which may not have been done and boundaries are to be regarded as approximate. Breeding distributions are shown in Figure 2.1 (page 20). Northern populations are migratory, so winter distribution differs and is shown in Figure 2.2. The key to the races on these maps follows.

A The nominate race *Falco tinnunculus tinnunculus*, breeding over most of Eurasia. Its eastern limit is the Kolyma river in eastern Siberia. In Scandinavia it reaches 70°N, but otherwise the northern boundary is roughly the July isotherm of 16°C (61°F) (Voous 1960). It also breeds in north Africa except Egypt. Many northern populations are migratory, wintering in the south of the Eurasian breeding range, Africa and India, Pakistan and Bangladesh; wintering birds also reach the Maldives and Laccadives.

B *F. t. interstinctus* Breeding in China, Japan, Korea and Tibet, and probably in Burma (Vaurie 1965). Stated by Vaurie to breed in Assam and the eastern Himalaya, but Salim Ali and Ripley (1978) note the evidence as unsatisfactory. Thus, the southern boundary of its breeding range is not certain. Partly migratory; wintering populations in India and Bangladesh, where the range overlaps that of wintering *tinnunculus* and resident *objurgatus*, south-east Asia and occasionally in the Philippines and Borneo. It does not, apparently, penetrate the breeding range of Moluccan Kestrel.

C *F. t. objurgatus* The only Kestrel breeding in peninsular India, where limited to hill country in the west; also breeds in Sri Lanka. Winter dispersal unknown (Salim Ali and Ripley 1978) but presumed resident. In peninsular India, the breeding season of this race overlaps with the presence of wintering *tinnunculus* (Salim Ali and Ripley 1978) and it would be interesting to know whether any habitat or other local segregation exists.

D *F. t. rupicolaeformis* Breeds in Egypt, northern Sudan and Arabia. Partly migratory (Brown, Urban and Newman 1982).

E *F. t. archeri* Breeds in Somalia and coastal Kenya and on the island of Socotra. Resident.

F *F. t. rufescens* Breeds from northern Guinea to the Ethiopian highlands and south to southern Tanzania and north Angola. Resident.

G *F. t. rupicolus* The rest of Africa south of the range of *rufescens*. Resident. Has the local name of Rock Kestrel in South Africa.

Kestrel hovering in a strong upcurrent along cliffs, 'spilling' the wind to hold its position, which alters its shape (see page 16).

H *F. t. canariensis* Breeds in Madeira and the western Canary Islands of Gran Canaria, Tenerife, Palma, Gomera and Hierro. Resident.

I *F. t. dacotiae* Breeds on the eastern Canaries: Fuerteventura, Lanzarote, and the small islands of Graciosa, Allegranza and Montaña Clara. Resident.

J *F. t. neglectus* Breeds on the northern Cape Verde Islands of Sal, Santo Antão, São Vicente, Razo and São Nicolau. Bannerman and Bannerman (1968) remarked that the species was declining markedly on the Cape Verde Islands and was scarce or absent on São Vicente, from where it may have disappeared in the late nineteenth century. Resident.

K *F. t. alexandri* The southern Cape Verde Islands of Brava, Fogo, São Tiago, Maio and Boa Vista. Resident.

Racial characteristics – plumage

Detailed museum descriptions of all these races can be found in standard accounts, and I have only summarized them here. The races *archeri* and *dacotiae* are paler than the nominate race, but other races tend to be darker, rather more brick-red or rich chestnut. The underparts are often darker and there is much variation in the size, extent and density of darker markings. The breeding range of these races extends into tropical or subtropical areas and the differences thus tend to follow Gloger's Rule, stating that races of species in warm, humid areas are apt to be more

19

Figure 2.1 *The breeding range of the Common Kestrel by race.*

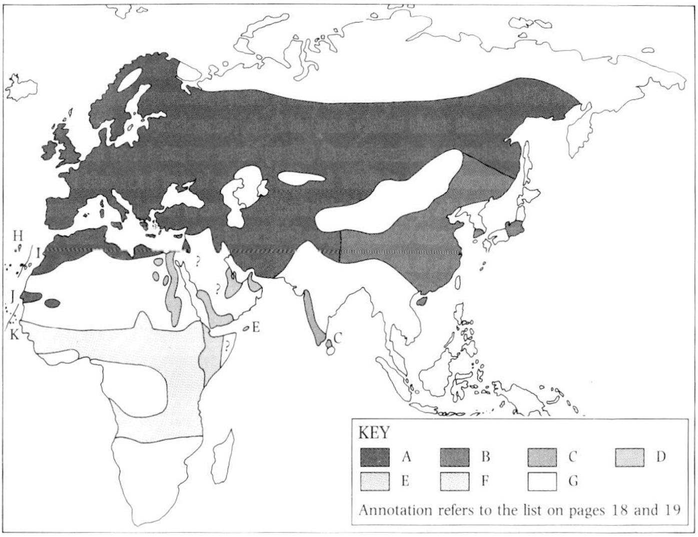

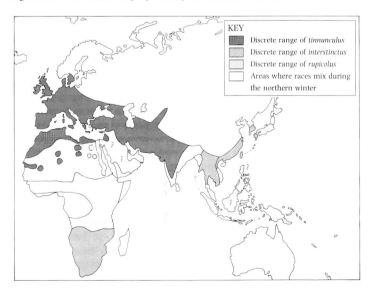

Data from Brown and Amadon 1968, Brown, Urban and Newman 1982, Cade 1982, Cramp and Simmons 1979, Salim Ali and Ripley 1978, and Vaurie 1965.

Figure 2.2 *The winter range of races of the Common Kestrel.*

Data from Brown and Amadon 1968, Brown, Urban and Newman 1982, Cade 1982, Cramp and Simmons 1979, Salim Ali and Ripley 1978, and Vaurie 1965.

heavily pigmented than in cold, dry areas (Thomson 1964). The plumage of the sedentary races also shows the same trend towards declining dimorphism as shown by sedentary kestrel species. Thus, in Africa, males of the race *rufescens* always show dark female-type barring to the grey tail and female *rupicolus* always has much grey about the head and a grey tail barred darker (Brown, Urban and Newman 1982). Males of the Indian race *objurgatus* have a duller grey head than the nominate race, often streaked rufous, and the tail is faintly barred (Salim Ali and Ripley 1978). Two of the island races show similar trends. The differences are slight but, as racial characteristics, they are presumably constant: those exhibited by *rufescens* and *rupicolus* should be detectable in the field (see plate 2, page 23).

Racial characteristics – size

Races vary quite markedly in size, with a fairly consistent decrease from continental and partly migratory through continental and sedentary to island forms. Wing measurements show that races are larger in the cooler parts of the range, thus conforming to Bergmann's Rule (Thomson 1964). They also show that size dimorphism may be distinctly less marked in migratory forms. It would be interesting to know if this results in differences in wing-loadings. It suggests the intriguing possibility that migratory forms have consistent aerodynamic differences.

Differences in ecology

Migratory races wintering in Africa overlap extensively with resident races. Thus, migrant *tinnunculus* and *rupicolaeformis* are found with resident *archeri* and *rufescens*. Brown, Urban and Newman (1982) suggest that these migrant populations differ in ecology in Africa. They are generally gregarious, whilst local residents are sedentary in pairs (and may be breeding when migrants are present), and they are also more insectivorous. These authors stress, however, that Kestrels have not been much studied in Africa. Such ecological separation would need to be confirmed by detailed studies. Nevertheless, their general observation contrasts with that of Salim Ali and Ripley (1978) for India, who stated that wintering birds are 'usually met with singly in well staked-out feeding territories', noting that they were frequently to be found roosting in the same site 'winter after winter'. Nor do these authors note a mainly insectivorous diet, recording a more typically generalized one. Over most of the Indian (and south-east Asian) wintering range of *tinnunculus* and *interstinctus*, however, there are no breeding populations of any kestrel species.

In both cases, it is tempting to point out that these ecological and distributional differences reduce the chances of competition between migrant and resident populations. Equally they may reflect it, and detailed study may give a different result. It would be particularly interesting to know if there are important variations in the behaviour of Palearctic migrants in those parts of East Africa where Brown (1970) found Kestrels inexplicably scarce breeding birds.

3

HABITAT
AND POPULATION

A S an open-country species, taking the bulk of its prey on the ground, the Kestrel needs grassland, plains, moorland and heathland habitats, savanna, open woodland, forestry plantations and farmland. Major forest clearings may be exploited, and Kestrels are increasingly utilizing urban habitats. They avoid dense forest and extreme desert. In many regions their numbers and distribution are strongly dependent on the availability of small diurnal mammals, in Europe mainly voles. Within this broad outline their presence may also be influenced by the availability of nest sites, for which they need features such as cliffs or buildings or trees or bushes. Cade (1982) suggests that there must be between one and two million pairs of Kestrels in their world range. There is, however, comparatively little detailed information on the species' natural history outside Britain and Europe, and this account now concentrates on these latter areas.

Habitat

In Britain and much of Europe the Kestrel is a bird of farmland in the broad sense of land used for agriculture, because this is the primary land use of open country. For example, farmland of some sort comprises 77 per cent of the total area of Britain and overall between 50 per cent and 60 per cent elsewhere in the EEC. Woodland of various kinds occupies 10 per cent of land in Britain and 27 per cent elsewhere in the EEC. Historically, Kestrels have undoubtedly benefited from the clearing of forest for agriculture throughout Europe and also from major land-reclamation schemes; the latter is still true in the Netherlands. The wooded areas include important Kestrel habitat such as young forestry plantation, but the total area is small compared with farmland and individual sites are only of temporary value. Kestrels have also extensively colonized cities. Farmland embraces several different land uses and habitats. In Britain detailed statistics are gathered annually. The farmland categories are defined as follows:

Rough grazing – unimproved permanent grassland, mainly unenclosed hill grazing, moorlands, some heathlands and lowland marshes. The category has no official definition but reflects the low levels of management applied.

Permanent grass – agriculturally improved grassland which has been established for five years or more.

Plumages of males and females in some races of the Common Kestrel, to show variations in the degree of sexual dimorphism (see page 21).

22

Falco tinnunculus tinnunculus
(male)

Falco tinnunculus tinnunculus
(female)

F. t. rufescens
(male)

F. t. rupicolus
(female)

Tillage – land that is cultivated annually (arable includes ley and is land that is cultivated in rotation). In Britain, tillage also includes permanent crops such as orchards, which comprise *c*. 1 per cent of the total area.

Ley – agriculturally improved grassland established for less than five years.

Other land in farmland includes hedges, tracks, farmsteads and similar sites, which are permanent features and not cultivated. Limited in area, they are often a significant for Kestrels, as they represent an important part of the habitat diversity available. An important feature of grassland habitats is how they are exploited for cattle and sheep. Farmland also includes an extensive but highly fragmented area of woodland, which averages 1.3 ha per farm in Britain.

Conifer forest is largely an upland habitat in Britain, and 70 per cent of the area has been planted since 1950 (Poore, 1983). Much has been planted on rough grazing and moorland habitats. Enclosing upland sheepwalks for forest results in a rapid increase in the density of the vegetation and often in large increases in voles. Kestrels quickly exploit such areas and, although the effects last only until the trees enclose the ground, extensive plantings will provide a succession of good Kestrel habitats for quite long periods.

Population estimates – Britain

Kestrel pairs can be surprisingly difficult to locate when nesting. Many county bird reports and avifaunas give some details of breeding numbers, but it is often unclear how complete they are. Table 3.1 summarizes counts of breeding Kestrels in Britain for the 1970s and 1980s for which I have been able to check the original references and which appear to provide fairly complete counts of the areas involved, together with my own records for Sussex and Breconshire. The estimates for single years should be regarded with caution, as breeding populations often fluctuate annually in any area.

The regional variations shown seem broadly to reflect land use. The highest densities were found in upland and pastoral districts of south-west Scotland, with large areas of rough grazing, low stocking rates and extensive young forestry providing good vole habitats. Probably many parts of northern England have similar densities, for land use is similar. The lowest densities were also in upland areas with high proportions of rough grazing and extensive forest, in Wales, where stocking rates, particularly of sheep, are twice as high, greatly reducing the value of rough grazing as vole habitat; much of the forest is older and unsuitable for Kestrels. In Breconshire it is now being widely felled and replanted, but I find few Kestrels in these restocked sites, although Buzzards are numerous.

Ratcliffe (1980) noted a long-term decline in bird populations in the western Highlands, a result of ecological degradation following intensive exploitation for sheep and deer in a very wet climate in the nineteenth century. This region has also shown a progressive decline in stocking rates since the 1870s (agricultural statistics), clear evidence of declining land quality. This presumably accounts for the low numbers of Kestrels found there. Upland birds are also declining rapidly in Wales as stocking rates of sheep rise steeply. Afforestation has contributed, however, and it is notable that the loss of heather moor in favour of sheep farming in the Welsh uplands has involved the disappearance of game-preserving. Some raptors are increasing as a result, which may lead to an important readjustment in the relative status of species such as Kestrel. In many Welsh areas, too, the typical raptor of open country is the Buzzard, which is often very numerous (26 pairs/100 km² in my Breconshire area, for example). Kestrels may compete unsuccessfully with Buzzards (page 74; Dare and Hamilton 1968; Dare 1986). High stocking rates, by limiting good vole habitat through grazing pressure, could well increase the significance of such competition. Much of western Britain also has a comparatively wet climate and, since rain inhibits hunting, this higher rainfall itself probably also contributes to lower Kestrel densities in many areas there, perhaps particularly if food supplies are less favourable. This may also be true for Ireland (see below).

In lowland farmland, in Table 3.1, numbers were very variable but tended to be highest in mixed farmland (i.e., where tillage and grassland enterprises were combined). Such differences probably partly reflect varying proportions of tillage, particularly cereals, the main crop. In Sussex, I found that hunting ranges in the breeding season expanded with the area of tillage (largely cereals) within them but showed no such tendency with the area of ley and permanent habitats (hedgeline, farmsteads, grassland, etc.). Pairs apparently needed an area of the order of 100 ha of the latter habitats to breed and presumably had to range more widely to find it in the

Table 3.1 *Recent population estimates for Kestrels in Britain.*

County and date	Habitat	Area (km²)	Number of pairs	Pairs/100km²	Reference
Sussex (Weald) 1978	Mixed farmland and woodland	405	65	16	Hughes and Dougharty (1979)
Sussex (Coast) 1979–82	Mixed and arable farmland	38	9–12	23–31	Shrubb (pers. obs.)
Leicestershire (Rutland) 1983–87	Mixed farmland	127	11–21	9–27	Village (1990)
Cambridgeshire 1984–87	Arable farmland	241	22–31	9–13	Village (1990)
Ayrshire 1970–78	Pastoral, upland and forestry	3000	750–1000	25–33	Riddle (1979)
Snowdonia 1975–82	Upland and some forestry	926	33–64	4–7	Dare (1986)
Breconshire 1985–90	Pastoral, upland and forestry	360	15–20	4–6	Shrubb (pers. obs.)
Dumfriesshire 1976–79	Upland grass and forestry	100	30–36	30–36	Village (1990)
Inverness 1968	Pastoral and upland	518	35	7	Scottish Bird Report 1969
Cheshire 1984	Dairying and mixed farmland	460	70	15	Cheshire Bird Report 1984

more extensively tilled parts of the area. Cereals especially were not used for hunting during the breeding season (Shrubb 1980), so sterilizing much of the birds' range for hunting at that period. As Kestrels are territorial in farmland, such a pattern is potentially likely to limit numbers. Pettifor (1983) made similar observations in arable farmland in Cambridgeshire.

Table 3.1 includes no area purely of intensively managed lowland-grassland farming, although the Cheshire area is an important dairying region. My observations in Wales, where virtually all lowland farmland qualifies, suggest that Kestrels would be scarce. Buzzards seem better able to exploit such habitat, and I have found Kestrels present in such areas only if there are substantial areas of bog or other rough ground. I have little doubt that for Kestrels, as for many birds in farmland, arable land is a better habitat than intensively managed grass monocultures. Presumably, the main reason for this is that mixed or arable farmland provides a richer variety of alternative prey to voles than does intensively managed grass.

The variations in density discussed above are also broadly supported by the New Breeding Atlas (Gibbons *et al.* in press). This shows fewer Kestrels in Wales, south-west England and north-west Scotland than elsewhere in Britain. The most consistently high numbers were recorded in East Anglia. Overall, its results suggest that the Kestrel is a lowland bird, although there were good numbers throughout much of northern England and southern Scotland. As forests grow, numbers in these latter areas may well decline.

So how many pairs are there? If the densities listed in Table 3.1 are reasonably typical, they suggest a population of the order of 30,000 to 37,000 pairs of Kestrels in Britain outside urban areas. Inevitably such calculations involve assumptions. I have assumed that numbers in Wales, south-west England and Cumbria, which are linked by features of land management and climate (and also hold substantially the highest Buzzard densities in Britain: Taylor *et al.* 1988), are probably similar. Similarities in habitat also seem to apply to much of southern Scotland and the rest of northern England, which I have again linked. Eastern Scotland is more intensively cultivated, and I have assumed densities similar to those in mixed farmland in lowland England. These may be rather high, as Buckland *et al.* (1990) noted a decline on the Buchan plain of north Aberdeen in the 1980s, attributed to agricultural changes. For the bulk of lowland England I have averaged the densities for mixed and arable farmland, and I have used the Inverness figure for the Scottish Highlands. Figure 3.1 shows a broad density distribution based on these assumptions. Density in any district may, of course, differ but I think it gives a clear idea of the variations over Britain.

Many Kestrels also breed in urban areas. A feature of this species' population in Britain during the past forty years has been a general spread into these habitats (Marchant *et al.* 1990). Recent counts include: in Greater London (3255 km^2), breeding proved in 233 tetrads (2-km squares) in 1968–72 (Montier 1977); in Sunderland, nine pairs (Durham Bird Report 1976); in Birmingham/Solihull/West Bromwich/Smethwick, 29 pairs (West Midlands Bird Report 1978); in Bristol, sixteen to 24 pairs (Avon Bird Report 1977); in Edinburgh, over forty pairs (Scottish Bird Report 1975); in Brighton, six pairs (Sussex Bird Report 1985). The species is stated to be 'common' in urban areas of Greater Manchester, and BTO nest record cards show it to be widespread in the industrial towns of north-west England and Yorkshire. It was increasing in urban Derbyshire in 1975 (Bird Report).

A survey in London also found high concentrations of pairs in some extensive open areas within the conurbation. These were: Richmond Park, nineteen nests on 1000 ha; Hampton Court Park/Bushy Park, seven pairs on 790 ha; Mitcham Common; seven pairs on 808 ha; and Kempton Park, three pairs on 150 ha (Montier 1968, Parr 1969). Parr stated that the Richmond Park birds hunted over neighbouring areas of suburban gardens, suggesting a situation analogous with that of many upland regions, where nesting areas may be clumped and feeding areas more widespread (Village 1983b). How widely this occurs in urban areas is unclear, but it has been noted in Ayrshire for example (Riddle 1979). There seems likely to be several thousand pairs of urban Kestrels in Britain so a total estimate of 35,000 to 40,000 pairs altogether is perhaps reasonable. Although numbers have declined since the early 1980s (Marchant et al. 1990), this is substantially fewer than the estimate of 70,000 pairs proposed by Newton (1984), presumably because of the low densities indicated here for much of western Britain. Furthermore, the New Atlas survey (Gibbons et al. in press) suggests

Figure 3.1 *Suggested regional densities of Kestrels breeding in Britain.*

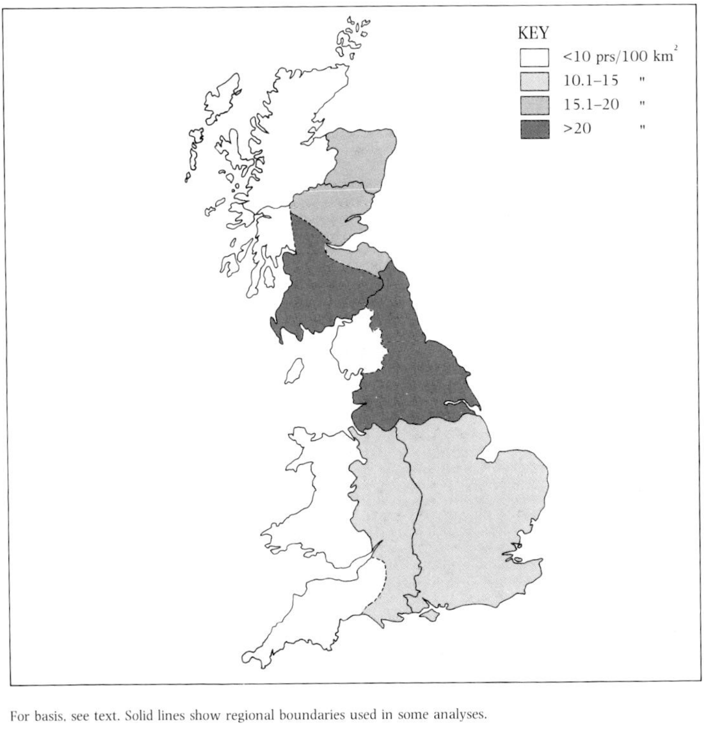

KEY

	<10 prs/100 km^2
	10.1–15 "
	15.1–20 "
	>20 "

For basis, see text. Solid lines show regional boundaries used in some analyses.

that seven pairs per 100 km^2 is far too high a density for much of the western Highlands, where a very large area now has very few Kestrels indeed.

In Ireland, the only recent estimate appears to be for Co. Wicklow, where Noonan (in Hutchinson 1989) recorded a density of about five pairs per 100 km^2. Gibbons *et al.* (in press) show that numbers in Ireland are lower than in Wales and rather uniform, so this figure may not be unrepresentative. It suggests a total Irish population of 4000–5000 pairs.

European populations

In continental Europe, densities appear to be generally lower than in Britain. Figure 3.2 plots those calculated for European countries where there are recent published estimates. An estimate for the whole of Europe, excluding Russia and the Baltic Republics, using these figures, gives a population of 192,000 to 340,000 pairs, of which Britain holds *c.* 15 per cent. A recent Russian estimate was of 3500 pairs in 270,000 km^2 of central Russia (Cramp and Simmons 1979).

In the EEC countries there is no obvious broad relationship between the variations in density shown in Figure 3.2 and forms of land use in each country. For Europe generally, however, variations may reflect differences in detailed knowledge of Kestrel numbers. The densities shown are also misleading in the sense that they do not necessarily apply to a given region of a country. For example, Cade (1982) remarked that Kestrels are generally scarce in extensive northern coniferous forest and, in Germany, breeding density was found to be related to winter temperature (Kostrzewa and Kostrzewa 1990). Presumably, such points account for the low numbers overall in Scandinavia although densities will be higher in suitable habitats, for example numbers in arable farmland in south-west Finland are comparable to those of lowland England (see Korpimäki 1986). Also, in most of mainland Europe, Kestrels tend to be part of a more extensive raptor community than exists in Britain, which may have an important bearing on numbers.

Changes in habitat and population – Britain

In Britain, the June Census of agriculture since 1866 has recorded marked changes in farmland habitats. These changes and their impact on birds were summarized by O'Connor and Shrubb (1986). Potentially the most significant to Kestrels seem to have been variations in the balance between grass and tillage, in stocking rates and in the proportion of tillage used for cereals. All these probably affect hunting terrain and food supplies. In the modern era, pesticides and hedge-loss have also been significant.

The first major period of change was the farming recession and then slump between the late 1870s and the 1930s. Grassland increased, to cover 80 per cent of English and Welsh farmland in the 1930s, a proportion without precedent. Unprecedented, too, was that land's neglect, particularly over lowland England where it was worsened by a collapse of land-drainage systems (Orwen and Whetham 1964). By the 1930s, south of a line roughly

Figure 3.2 *European Kestrel density (pairs/100 km²) by country. It does not breed in Iceland.*

KEY
No information
<1 pr/100 km²
<5   "
<10   "
>15   "

Data from Chancellor (ed.) 1977, Cramp and Simmons 1979, Gensbøl 1989, and Newton and Chancellor (eds) 1985.

from the Severn to the Humber, stocking rates had fallen by 30–50 per cent of the 1870s levels. Elsewhere in Britain stock numbers rose in line with the expanding grass area, so stocking rates stagnated. They had always decreased towards the north and west, however, and those in Scotland were still less than half the depleted levels of lowland England.

Such changes were potentially important to Kestrels, for grazing pressure by and management for domestic stock have a major influence on the nature of grassland swards. Rough, poorly managed or lightly grazed grassland provides good habitat for voles (Corbet and Southern 1977), which are important to Kestrels, and vice versa. It is certain that, among other features, the decline in farming in the early twentieth century caused a major increase in the availability of good vole habitats in English farmland.

World War II and the ensuing agricultural revolution reversed this trend, and the broad composition of farmland is again near that of Victorian England. This reversal, however, brought three major changes in farm-land's basic character. One is a massive increase in stocking rates, which have more than doubled since the 1930s. Latterly this has in particular involved a spectacular increase in sheep in England and Wales, of *c.* 35 per cent in the 1980s alone. This intensification of grazing pressure, together with repairing and improving land drainage, reseeding, fertilizing and other pasture improvement, has again fundamentally altered the character of many grassland habitats throughout England and Wales and cut back good vole habitats within them. Such changes have been less marked in Scotland, where climatic considerations (which affect stocking rates), the dominance of rough moorland grazings in farmland and competing economic interests of grouse-shooting and deer-stalking modify the scope for such changes. An emerging problem may be the untrammelled increase in deer numbers now occurring there (e.g., Watson 1991). In the uplands at the same time, c. 1,000,000 ha, mainly of rough grassland and moorland, have been planted for forestry. In the long term this represents habitat loss for Kestrels, despite plantations being good Kestrel habitat in their early years.

The second change has been the steady process of specialization on farms, which has greatly reduced habitat diversity. Most improved farmland in the Victorian era combined arable crops and stock, producing a great mixture of habitat. Declining diversity reduces both the variety and the volume of potential prey animals available: it may also render prey more

Just airborne; a fine adult male Kestrel soon after take-off, showing the underwing pattern well.

difficult to catch because there is less varied cover (see chapter 4). One result of modern trends has been an increasing split in England and Wales to an arable east and a pastoral west. At their extremes counties such as Cambridgeshire have 90 per cent of farmland in tillage, while Wales has a similar proportion in grass. Particular crops or stock dominate regions: cereals, for example, now form 50–60 per cent of all farmland in East Anglia and much of the East Midlands and even higher proportions in some districts of the south and south Midlands, compared with c. 30 per cent in the 1930s. Such dominance by cereals must, I believe, restrict Kestrels. Sheep increasingly dominate farming in Wales, where stocking rates are higher than in any other region. Tightly grazed sheep pastures are as little used by breeding Kestrels for hunting as are cereals.

The third change, the major reorganization of fields, mainly in lowland England, has resulted in a loss of habitat amounting to c. 174,600 km of hedgeline (Joyce *et al.* 1988) and it is a habitat used particularly often for hunting by breeding Kestrels in farmland (page 53). Hedge loss may affect habitat in more subtle ways, for changes in field size may affect the pattern and distribution of crops through rotations. Crops move into larger and less well-distributed parcels, which is another source of declining diversity.

Modern farming systems are also based on the development and use of chemical pesticides to replace rotations and cultivations for controlling pests, diseases and weeds. Pesticide use is ultimately the most significant feature of the modern agricultural revolution, less because of toxicity problems, although these are important, than because they make the rest possible.

Despite the scale of habitat change in the Kestrel's world, we have very little idea of what effect it had in the late nineteenth and early twentieth centuries. This is largely because the major impact on all raptors then was human persecution. For Kestrels few comparative counts exist to measure this. Ornithologists tended to concentrate on the larger and rarer species.

Some general points can be made, however. In Britain, raptor persecution became most systematic in the late eighteenth and the nineteenth centuries with the fashion for large-scale game-preserving, the increase in gamekeepers that resulted, improved firearms and the insistence of landowners on the destruction of species considered vermin. It is clear from early accounts that the last was important. Landowners encouraged and co-ordinated the destruction, often running private bounty schemes, much as other European countries ran government ones. The concentration of land in comparatively few hands was probably a significant factor in the persecution's scale and impact. In 1877, for example, over half the land in England and Wales was held by 4217 private landowners, and over 40 per cent by 1688; 85 per cent of all farmholdings were rented (Grigg 1989). This gave a strong element of uniformity in matters such as game management, which was enhanced by competition over bag sizes. It was probably the introduction of driven-game shooting around the 1850s, and the importance then given to bag size, that led to greater persecution of small raptors such as Kestrels.

Persecution especially affected breeding pairs, because gamekeepers concentrate on predator control in the breeding season. Large numbers of Kestrels were known to be killed, and the literature contains some

31

gruesome lists of raptors killed on various estates in Wales and Scotland. A typical one, given by Forrest (1907), included a total of 1988 Kestrels killed on the Penrhyn estates in north Wales between 1874 and 1902, an average of 71 per year. If all were breeding, present densities suggest that this would wipe out the equivalent of the breeding population on 500 km² annually, and such effects may have been quite regular on strictly preserved estates. Despite the lack of figures, all late nineteenth- and early twentieth-century accounts agree that persecution depressed numbers and all give the overriding impression that Kestrels, although widespread, were rather scarce compared with today. This is reinforced by the frequent statements of marked increase or recovery following the decline in large-scale game-preserving after World Wars I and II. Some accounts, e.g., Newton (1896) generally, Lilford (1895) for Northamptonshire and Haines (1907) for Rutland, describe Kestrels as mainly summer visitors in lowland England. Haines also especially remarked a scarcity of adults among breeding birds, indicating that these were mainly immature. This is in marked contrast to modern experience (see Village 1990) and suggests a pattern of young birds regularly attempting to recolonize vacant territories. These patterns undoubtedly reflected the impact of systematic persecution.

Kestrels rarely take gamebird chicks in the wild. I have only one record from prey remains and have only once seen one try it. A male was circling low over a covey of Grey Partridge chicks but the cock partridge held him off by jumping up at him and the hen shepherded the chicks to safety in a nearby wheatfield. Such active defence may be why game chicks are taken rarely, but wader chicks frequently; the latter freeze while the adults mob the predator to drive it away. Data from Europe (references in Table 4.2) indicated that gamebird chicks comprised only 1 per cent of vertebrate items taken in the breeding season, although birds comprised 22 per cent.

Kestrels came to be regarded as pests by gamekeepers because of the effect on gamebird chick predation of the layout and management of Pheasant-rearing fields in the nineteenth and early twentieth centuries. In these the fostering hens were kept cooped, while the chicks ran about outside in enclosures, thus deprived of protection and highly vulnerable (Ticehurst 1932). In an attempt to assess such predation, Menteith Ogilvie examined the stomach contents of 59 Kestrels, of which 60 per cent were males, sent to him by gamekeepers during May, June and July during 1893–1917, mainly from east Suffolk. Of these, 42 per cent had taken Pheasant chicks, which comprised 25 per cent of the food items found (Ticehurst 1932; data labels, British Museum). These were just what these birds had eaten themselves, but many were also feeding mates or broods and several were shot as they carried chicks off; Ogilvie also had records of, for example, 'a male taking a dozen chicks in a morning', all at rearing fields. Other local avifaunas of the period report similar behaviour. Ogilvie also noted that Sparrowhawks were far less prone to conduct such raids (Ticehurst 1932). It is easy to see how such experience could lead to game-keepers regarding Kestrels as particular threats during the breeding season

The first reports of a change in attitude towards Kestrels by game-preserving interests coincide with the vole plagues of 1891–93 in the Borders.

Voles caused serious economic damage to upland sheep grazings over an area of c. 2400 km² in Dumfries, Roxburgh, Selkirk, Peebles and Lanark (Picozzi and Hewson 1970). Contemporary authors (e.g., Gladstone 1910) ascribed the eruption to the lack of natural vole predators such as Kestrels. Whatever the cause of the outbreak, it is noticeable that accounts for Scotland after this period note a greater tolerance of Kestrels in upland districts.

Attitudes towards the management of field sports have continued to change and in Britain today Kestrel populations are not generally affected by persecution, although it does occur (e.g., Easy 1990), and Cadbury (1991) recorded that 8 per cent of the birds of prey reported as poisoned, shot or trapped in the United Kingdom during 1979–89 were Kestrels. Nevertheless, Marchant et al. (1990) note a general increase since 1945, which may reflect a decline in persecution by game-preserving interests.

It is in the modern era in Britain, however, that habitat change and pesticide use may have most influenced Kestrel numbers, although the impact of habitat change has been little studied. Newton (1984) suggested that many habitats had reached their carrying capacity. This was certainly well below that of pre-1945 farmland in Britain. Assuming both that the higher densities recently found in pastoral and upland areas were common then to predominantly grassland regions outside the north-west Highlands and that densities in mixed farmland were at the top end of the present range, because of the much greater area of good vole habitat throughout farmland, a potential pre-1945 total of c. 55,000–60,000 pairs can be estimated. This may be an overestimate, for the high densities in upland areas today reflect the presence of extensive forestry planted after 1945. Nevertheless, I believe that this figure gives an idea of the likely scale of population change stemming from modern changes in agricultural habitats.

Any such decline has been partly offset by the expansion into urban areas. For example, very few Kestrels bred in the London area in the 1930s but they were widespread by the 1960s (Montier 1977). There is, however, no proof that this expansion has been based on birds displaced by habitat changes elsewhere, although that is possible.

Since 1962, the Common Birds Census (CBC) of the BTO has shown that Kestrels reached a low point in the early 1960s, recovering and remaining at a high level during the late 1960s and 1970s, then declining again in the 1980s. The recent decline is due largely to a decrease in Wales and western England (Marchant et al. 1990). This regional decline ties in well with the idea that the impact of high stocking rates on grassland habitats and therefore on voles limits Kestrels, for these regions are primarily grass farmland and very heavily stocked. This idea is supported by Ratcliffe's (1990) observation that competition by sheep has reduced the scale of vole cycles in upland sheepwalk (see also Village 1990 Figure 2), by German observations that agricultural intensification has suppressed vole cycles in Westphalia (Kostrzewa and Kostrzewa 1990) and by the analysis of Snow (1968). Snow showed that the numbers of nestlings ringed annually in Britain fluctuated in line with known vole cycles, but noted that, after the 1940s, such fluctuations were only visible in northern Britain, mainly Scotland. This is the area least affected by rising stocking rates in upland

33

grazing. Comparing the two Atlas surveys shows an increase from 1.5 per cent of 10-km squares unoccupied in 1968–72 to 6 per cent in 1989–91 in Wales and south-west England (Sharrock 1976; Gibbons *et al.* in press). Such differences are even more marked in Ireland, another area of increasingly intensively managed grass monocultures (90 per cent of farmland is grass): unoccupied 10-km squares increased from 2 per cent to 21 per cent between the two surveys. This period exactly coincides with Ireland's access to the EEC's Common Agricultural Policy (CAP) and has seen a rapid modernization of agriculture; stocking rates have increased by 2.5 times (Hutchinson 1989). Ireland, however, lacks *Microtus* voles so that the impact of such changes on the Kestrel's ecology there may differ from that in Britain. Such differences could also be influenced by climate, particularly rainfall. Both south-west Scotland and central Wales, however, have similarly

Pheasant chicks in an old-style rearing field. With the hens cooped they were very vulnerable to Kestrels (see page 32).

wet climates: Kestrels are far more numerous in the former (and lay larger clutches earlier: page 89), pointing to habitat as the main difference.

Pesticides may have had a limited long-term impact on Kestrel numbers in Britain. Organochlorine pesticides, such as DDT, appear to have affected breeding performance rather little compared with their effect on Sparrowhawks or Peregrines. Raptors that feed on mammals are less exposed to such substances because they top shorter food chains, and because mammals are better able to excrete toxic substances; mammals are also less mobile than birds, so that their predators are likely to be exposed to pesticides through them only near the point of use (Newton 1979, 1986).

Nevertheless, Kestrels declined very sharply in the early 1960s in the eastern counties of England (Prestt 1965; Parslow 1973), and it was a decline much greater than might have been expected from habitat changes, although these must have contributed. Its regional nature, too, indicated that it was not caused by the severe winter of 1962/63, which was general in its effects. In fact county bird reports suggest the nadir was reached in 1960–62. Despite appeals for records the numbers then reported in counties from Lincoln to Kent and west to Nottingham, Bedford and Hertford were tiny – 73 pairs in nine counties totalling 28,000 km². These do not pretend to be complete counts but they do hint at the scale of the decline. As a birdwatcher who was very active in the late 1950s and early 1960s, I can attest to the amount of concern and fieldwork which worries about the effects of chemical pesticides generated. The same local reports were recording a substantial recovery in the mid 1970s, which Village (1990) noted as continuing in the 1980s. The pattern of decline and recovery was, in fact, very similar to that described for Sparrowhawks by Newton and Haas (1984), and presumably it was similarly caused by the use and then progressive phasing-out of seed-dressings of the cyclodienne group of organochlorine pesticides, particularly dieldrin. These were highly toxic substances and acted as direct poisons to predators as they accumulated lethal doses from their prey.

Newton *et al.* (1991) have shown that cyclodiennes were an important cause of mortality among Barn Owls in arable farmland in eastern England in the 1960s and 1970s, pointing out that the owl was exposed to dressed seed through its reliance on Wood Mice and rats in such habitats. Both eat cereal grains and both are also widely taken by Kestrels in the same habitats. Kestrels also take many birds in farmland, particularly seed-eating passerines (page 43), and moribund birds would have been especially tempting targets.

In the uplands of northern England and Scotland, at least, Kestrel populations also vary in response to vole numbers, which fluctuate over an approximately four-year cycle (Snow 1968). Ratcliffe (1990) noted that such vole cycles never produce very high numbers on sheepwalk today because of grazing pressure by sheep. Eruptions of voles also seem to be rather local, and it seems unlikely that the fluctuations they cause now have a very marked effect on overall Kestrel numbers. Afforestation produces rather similar effects on vole populations, which also attracts Kestrels. As forests grow I would expect changes in the numerical distribution of Kestrels, particularly in Scotland, where most new planting now occurs (Forestry Commission statistics).

Habitat and population changes – Europe

There have also been substantial changes in the basic areas of habitat in western Europe since 1955. Farmland in the continental countries covered by EEC statistics has declined by *c.* 13,000,000 ha (17 per cent) and the wooded area has increased by *c.* 7,200,000 ha (28 per cent), thus reversing historic trends. Changes in the farmland area have been uniform across the different categories (page 22), but cereals have increased as a proportion of tillage by about 7 per cent (760,000 ha). In the Netherlands, land area has increased by 181,000 ha with reclamation from the sea.

Throughout Europe, also, farmland has been subject to the same processes of intensification and specialization noted for Britain during the period. In the EEC this has been promoted by its Common Agricultural Policy (CAP), and its recent export to Mediterranean countries such as Spain and Portugal, where extensive areas of scarce and sensitive habitats remain, managed by a traditional and conservative agriculture has, perhaps, been peculiarly damaging. There its effects extend to the wooded area, with traditional habitats being cleared for commercial pine and eucalyptus plantation, habitat infinitely poorer in diversity and species (L. Palma, in Newton and Chancellor 1985).

Bijleveld (1974) provided evidence that Kestrels have declined in virtually every European country, a conclusion supported by other reports. The main causes of decline are summarized in Table 3.2 which is limited to those countries providing some information directly related to Kestrels. The impact of these factors probably extends beyond the limits of these lists, for other reports note that persecution and pesticides form major threats to raptors generally. In some countries – Denmark, the Netherlands, Sweden, Hungary, Belgium and also Switzerland – the pattern of decline and recovery resembles that in Britain, but this seems by no means universal and accounts leave the impression that recovery has generally been incomplete.

Of the main causes listed in Table 3.2, climatic effects have been noted as more than temporary only in Finland, where increasingly harsh winters have been suggested as causing a marked population decline in Kestrels (P. Saurola, in Génsbøl 1989). This links with German observations of a relationship between breeding density and winter temperature (page 28). Habitat change in Mediterranean countries is related to rapid industrial development and the industrialization of agriculture following entry to the EEC. France has also experienced extensive habitat changes from the former, but, in north-west Europe, only the Netherlands and Denmark have specifically related changes in agricultural habitats to a decline in Kestrels. This may be because these effects have been subsumed in declines ascribed to pesticides, as they have tended to be in Britain; the two are closely linked. Several authors note that industrialization in southern Europe has led to rural depopulation, which has been of some benefit to raptors.

Most attention has focused on persecution and pesticides. The accounts I have examined indicate that their effects have been more marked than in Britain. With pesticides there is an important ecological difference in much of temperate Europe compared with lowland farmland in Britain. Britain lacks the Common Vole, which is the widespread vole of cultivated land on the continent (Van den Brink 1967). One result of this was that continental countries conducted campaigns to control them in the 1950s and 1960s, using poisoned grain baits spread on fields. Such campaigns were recorded in Denmark, France, Germany, Hungary and Spain; and the substances used included thallium sulphate, phosphide, aldrin, endrin and toxaphene, the last three all highly toxic organochlorines (W. Przygodda, in ICBP 1964). Just how effective such campaigns can be in incidentally destroying raptor populations has been shown in Israel, where the wide-scale use of rodenticides in this way virtually extirpated rodent-eating raptors, without materially affecting the pests targeted (Newton 1979). It is unlikely that such use of rodenticides failed to contribute to declines in Kestrels in Europe, although details are unclear. How much their use continues is also unclear, but they were reported as still used in Spain in the mid 1970s, when they particularly affected owl populations (Garzon 1977). Kostrzewa and Kostrzewa (1990) also noted that intensive farming and pest control in Westphalia had suppressed vole cycles. In Spain and Portugal it is the increased use of insecticides as agriculture becomes modernized that has been reported as most affecting Kestrels (J. Garzon, in Chancellor 1977; L. Palma, in Newton and Chancellor 1985) because the species is strongly insectivorous, as in many parts of southern Europe. The effects of such pesticides have been even more marked on Lesser Kestrels.

Mercurial seed-dressings have been among the most widely used of all pesticides in farming, and mercury was specifically linked to a decline in Kestrels in Sweden in the 1950s and 1960s; incidents involving mercurial poisoning were also noted in Denmark and the Netherlands. Often any effects of mercury may have been masked by the effects of organochlorine pesticides, but more than one type of mercury compound has been used as a seed-dressing and it was particularly methyl-mercury that proved dangerous to birds (Newton 1979). Its withdrawal led to a recovery in Kestrels in Sweden; it does not appear to have been used in Britain.

Raptor persecution has also differed in important respects in the rest of Europe compared with Britain. Most European countries operated state-financed bounty schemes for the destruction of birds of prey well into this century. Often aimed at particular species, they were widely abused. More important, perhaps, is the whole ethos of shooting, particularly in southern Europe. Most Mediterranean countries have long traditions of songbird-trapping and hunters regard any bird as fair game. Table 3.2 shows clearly that the persecution that has recently been noted particularly for Kestrels is concentrated mainly in France and Mediterranean Europe. Several authors

Table 3.2 *Reported causes of decline in Kestrel populations in Europe by country*

	Belgium	Denmark	Finland	France	Greece	Hungary	Italy	Malta	The Netherlands	Portugal	Romania	Spain	Sweden
Persecution	x			x	x		x	x		x		x	
Pesticides		x	x	x		x			x	x	x	x	x
Habitat changes	(x)	x		(x)	(x)				x			x	
Climatic changes	x		x	x					x				

Notes: ( ) indicates a general statement said to apply to all raptors
Sources: ICBP 1964; Chancellor 1977; Newton and Chancellor 1985; Bijleveld 1974; P. Saurola in Génsbøl 1989.

have recorded with concern that rapidly increasing numbers of hunters are pursuing declining stocks of game, with the result that they shoot anything, even butterflies according to a recent correspondent in *Birds* magazine.

A traditional method was to shoot raptors over Eagle Owl decoys, a method perhaps peculiarly likely to attract Kestrels, which are very apt to mob other raptors. In France and Belgium it was also noted that Kestrels were attracted to bird-trappers' call decoys (E. Kesteloot and H. Wille: J-F. Terrasse, in ICBP 1964). It is unlikely that the latter no longer happens. In some countries raptor-shooting is regarded as a distinct sport. In Sicily, for example, it has its own season, recently expanded and always ignored and coinciding with the migration of raptors through the island (Massa 1977). Thus the persecution they inflict is exported to other countries.

The overall effects of persecution today are difficult to assess. In Catalonia. illegal persecution has been cited as an important factor affecting Buzzard and Kestrel populations. It is always difficult, however, in an era when several major factors such as habitat change, pesticides and persecution are operating simultaneously, accurately to separate the influence of one. Such gaps are invariably exploited by vested interests to dodge remedial action.

Conservation

It is unlikely that the Kestrel will ever become an endangered species. It is too adaptable, occupies too large a geographic range, and breeds in too wide a range of climates and habitats, and specific conservation measures are difficult to suggest. These normally need a focus – rarity or precise habitat requirements, for example. There is little need for such measures for Kestrels.

In considering Man's impact on birds of prey generally and Kestrels in particular, the themes of habitat change, pesticide use and persecution recur continually. Despite this species' general adaptability, there is no doubt that it has been and still is significantly affected by these factors at least on a regional basis. This should be a matter of concern.

For Kestrels, major impacts of habitat change tend to be linked to changes in farming methods. In northern and western Europe at least, therefore, the present trend towards winding down agriculture will probably benefit Kestrels. In Britain, lowering stocking rates in Environmentally Sensitive Areas (ESAs) in the uplands and taking lowland farmland out of production by 'set aside' should improve the availability of vole habitats and see an increase in food and habitat resources for Kestrels and many other species.

Perhaps this should not yet be regarded as a lasting benefit. 'Set aside' as currently managed is creating new habitats, not recreating old ones, and the effects of this may not be fully understood. Nor is it certain that the taxpayer will continue to support such ideas. The present fashion in Britain is for farmers to do anything with their land except that for which they are temperamentally and technically equipped – growing crops. Are many alternative schemes for making farm assets pay really economically viable, however, or, in terms of wildlife conservation, necessarily an improvement on agriculture? Many of our most prized habitats are actually the product of forms of farm management. I remain sceptical of whether the present fashion will last or whether any lasting benefit will come of it.

In southern Europe, too, entry to the EEC is having the opposite effect, with major changes being wrought in agricultural habitats as farming is modernized with little obvious regard for need or for the lessons of the north. Without doubt, if this policy works, the resulting overproduction will lead to artificial methods, such as quotas or ESAs, being introduced to control it. Nothing could so aptly typify the barren futility of such bureaucratic meddling in land management. The most profound habitat changes have been wrought with taxpayers' money, not for economic reasons, but for political advantage.

Although the dangers of pesticides are increasingly clearly understood, it would be foolish to believe that, in an era when agriculture largely depends on them, another crisis, similar to that caused for raptors by organochlorines, cannot recur. Nor are pesticides likely to be banned. In Spain and Portugal, agricultural insecticides have been particularly cited as seriously affecting Kestrels by reducing the volume of their insect prey. Such indirect effects are much more difficult to combat than the more obvious and dramatic results of direct poisoning. It is this kind of indirect effect which could emerge elsewhere on a wider scale as chemical pest control continues to expand, both geographically and in the range of pests targeted. Biological methods of pest control may be less harmful but agricultural pests may also be food sources for birds, so this is by no means certain. Nor am I convinced that we really understand the ramifications of biological pest control in the open countryside, particularly if this involves using alien predatory insects. Nevertheless, for Kestrels, such indirect effects of pesticides are likely to be restricted to regions where the falcons' diet is limited. Where they regularly take a wide range of prey they are far less vulnerable. Historically, however, human persecution has been the most significant and widespread factor affecting Kestrel populations. It is disturbing, therefore, to note that some Mediterranean populations are now apparently being sharply reduced by hunting. These are the populations which can now least withstand it, particularly as the number of hunters in the region is increasing rapidly.

The control of persecution and reducing the destructive impact of policies such as the CAP are the measures which seem most likely to be effective in conserving a species such as the Kestrel. They are matters for government legislation. So far as protection of the Kestrel is concerned, that legislation is in place in most European countries, and it is now simply a matter of enforcement. Only by helping to raise public awareness, concern and acceptance of the problems caused and by exerting pressure to deal with them does it seem likely that the individual can effectively advance this. No one should suppose that it will be easy or quick.

4

FOOD AND HUNTING

THE diet of the Kestrel has been widely studied in Europe, although methods have varied, making strict statistical comparisons between areas and seasons rather difficult. Nevertheless, there is good general agreement in these studies, which clearly give a fair picture of the diet.

Over most of north and west Europe Kestrels feed primarily on small mammals, mainly *Microtus* voles, which are active throughout the day (Corbet and Southern 1977). It would be wrong, however, to regard them as specialists in such prey, a term which implies necessity. Where voles are absent they concentrate on other small mammals, small birds, reptiles and insects. In most areas the diet in fact combines several such elements. The basic requirement is that there should be a sufficiency of small animals that can be caught on the ground. Kestrels can and do take birds in flight, and may take bats with some regularity (Cramp and Simmons 1979); they also frequently hawk flying insects. They rarely pursue prey, however, the consequence of the aerodynamic limitations discussed on page 12. The general rule is usually one attack, kill or miss, and depart.

Cramp and Simmons (1979) record a minimum of 23 mammal species in the diet, and at least eight more were noted for the Soviet Union by Dementiev and Gladkov (1951). Generally speaking, this wide range reflects the Kestrel's own wide geographical range, as various *Microtus* voles, for example, replace each other in different regions. In any one region the mammals taken tend to be dominated by just a few species: in Britain the Short-tailed Vole, and over much of temperate Europe the Common Vole. The weight of the mammals commonly preyed upon by Kestrels falls into the range 4–25 g, at least in Britain (Yalden 1977), but they are able to kill larger animals. Young rabbits, leverets, weasels and Red and Grey Squirrels have all been recorded, and I found that rats were taken regularly on my Sussex farm, nearly always in spring and autumn. Tooth wear showed these to be mostly young animals, but I watched one female Kestrel dealing with a rat which was too heavy for her to do more than drag along. Vole populations are cyclic and, when voles are scarce in areas where they constitute the main prey, Kestrels periodically turn to other prey, perhaps particularly shrews, birds and insects.

The bird prey of Kestrels is equally varied, but again, in any area, a few species dominate. In the Netherlands Cavé (1968) recorded a minimum of 28 species, but 71 per cent of his records involved Starlings. In Sussex I recorded at least sixteen species, but seed-eating passerines, especially sparrows, formed 48 per cent of those identified, Starlings 24 per cent and Skylarks 22 per cent. Seed-eaters could often be detected by palatal thickenings in pellets (Yalden and Warburton 1979) but not more specifically identified. They comprised 22 per cent of unidentified bird prey and often vied with Short-tailed Voles as the most frequent vertebrate prey item. Skylarks were abundant winter visitors and were important at that season, as were Starlings, but newly fledged Starlings were also important prey for Kestrels feeding young in the nest. In some years Kestrels are serious predators of wader and tern chicks. In Sussex I did not record this annually on the same scale, but, when Kestrels turned to them, Lapwing chicks were obviously taken in some numbers. In the uplands, Kestrels take many juvenile birds for their young, particularly Meadow Pipits. Clearly, during the nestling stage of the breeding cycle, newly fledged birds are an important food source for Kestrels, as they are for species such as Merlins and Sparrowhawks.

An insight into the scale on which breeding Kestrels take bird prey in Britain is provided by incidental data on prey on the BTO's nest record cards. I found such data on 112 cards scattered through the period 1950–87 and from all over Britain; 68 per cent recorded bird prey and 50 per cent mammals (some had both). A total of 257 birds was recorded, together with seventeen records of unspecified numbers. Twenty-five species were identified, but juvenile Starlings comprised 56 per cent, seed-eating passerines 19 per cent, thrushes 8 per cent and Meadow Pipits 5 per cent. Of 119 mammals (plus eleven records of unspecified numbers), 56 per cent were Short-tailed Voles. Moles and rats combined to supply a surprising 20 per cent of records, which may reflect their interest to observers more than the frequency with which Kestrels caught them.

These data are probably biased towards bird prey because bird remains are more durable and obvious, but they suggest how widely and regularly Kestrels prey on birds in the breeding season. I find it difficult to avoid the conclusion that in the breeding season, and in farmland more generally, birds are major prey for British Kestrels. Only in spring is this not so in lowland farmland in my experience. I agree with Village (1990) that at that season only voles are sufficiently abundant (or perhaps catchable) in farmland to allow breeding: the winter influx of small birds has then dispersed and the summer flush of gormless young is not yet available.

In Sussex, the average size of bird prey identified was 38 g, twice the size of the average mammal item. The largest bird I recorded was a Collared Dove taken by a female around a grain store, a bird of about 75 per cent of the Kestrel's weight. Yalden (1980) found that Kestrels preyed on pigeon squabs in Manchester, and the nest record cards note an apparently freshly killed Stock Dove, a young Moorhen and a fully grown Lapwing. Other records of birds of similar size are scattered through the literature.

The greater average size of bird prey than mammal prey boosts its importance in the diet. Birds formed only 36 per cent of vertebrate prey items I counted for my Sussex Kestrels, but they formed 53 per cent by weight. Weight, however, is a misleading criterion of importance here, for birds and mammals may have proportionately different calorific values. J.G. Kirkwood (in Cramp and Simmons 1979) found that Kestrels kept in captive conditions ate about 36 g of day-old chick or 19 g of laboratory mouse per day, the difference reflecting variations in fat content and roughage of the prey. The same principle will apply in the wild, although the difference between mammals and fully grown birds will be less marked. Taking weight as the main criterion of the importance of prey items may be misleading in another way. Nearly every European study of the Kestrel's food notes the presence of insects in the diet and many British ones have noted pellets containing significant amounts of dirt and sand, a sign that earthworms had been taken. I believe that the importance of insects has been underestimated. Table 4.1 summarizes the insect diet enumerated in eight European studies (The lepidoptera recorded were all caterpillars, the hymenoptera largely ants and the dermaptera were earwigs). Most of these studies were based on pellet analysis, which underestimates invertebrate prey. For example, Kestrels take many craneflies in autumn, besides items such as dragonflies and adult moths. These leave few traces. I have also watched Kestrels join Black-headed Gulls to hawk flying ants but failed to find evidence of these in pellets. Earthworms were regularly recorded in the English studies and comprised a minimum of 5 per cent of the total diet by weight in both.

Although Kestrels may run about on the ground to pick up small prey items, an impression given by any attempt to enumerate insect prey is that they must often spend a disproportionate amount of time pursuing individually small prey items. This is perhaps characteristic of young birds, and it seems possible that the nutritional value of insect prey to Kestrels may be greater than simple considerations of size and weight suggest.

Table 4.1 *The insect diet of the Kestrel in different parts of Europe. The figures are the numbers of items recorded.*

| | FINLAND | ENGLAND | | | FRANCE | | | ITALY |
		Lakes[2]	Sussex[3]	North[3]	Camargue[5]	Corsica[6]	Vendée[7]	
Dermaptera			27	28			9	
Orthoptera	2	189	119	167	4194	632	132	92
Hemiptera	4							
Lepidoptera	2	773	48					
Hymenoptera	156							27
Coleoptera					868	318	308	
Dung beetles and chafers	12	316	36	5				1
Ground beetles and others	491	205	1144	142				12
Other orders		4	85		16	1		7
Insects as a percentage of total items taken	25	84	36	32	90	86	9	82

Sources: [1] Itämies and Korpimäki 1987; [2] Yalden and Warburton 1979; [3] Shrubb 1980 and unpublished; [4] Thiollay 1963; [5] and [7] Thiollay 1968a; [6] Thiollay 1968b; [8] Lovari 1974.

Geographical variations in diet

There are important geographical variations in the prey of Kestrels,
and Table 4.2 summarizes a series of studies to illustrate this. Some of
these studies were based on pellet analysis and some on stomach contents,
and not all were done at the same time of year or covered the whole year,
so conclusions must be drawn with caution. Certain broad patterns are
very clear, however, and those summarized in the table are supported by
other studies which have expressed prey by percentages (e.g., Davis 1975;
Simms 1961; Village 1990).

The regional variations shown in Table 4.2 seem basically explicable
by the distribution and abundance of Common Voles. Where numerous
in temperate Europe these dominate the Kestrel's diet to a much greater
extent than any single prey item does elsewhere. In Britain and
Scandinavia, where the Common Vole does not occur except in southern
Finland (Van den Brink 1967), Short-tailed Voles are the most frequent
item, but a much greater variety of vertebrate prey is characteristic and, in
Britain at least, includes more birds than in other European areas.
In Ireland, where there are few voles of any species, the prey are
dominated by Wood Mice, and birds and beetles are regular prey in winter
(Fairley and Maclean 1965; Fairley 1973). In Mediterranean Europe, where
Microtus voles again have a limited distribution, invertebrates, particularly
orthoptera, dominate the diet and reptiles become of greater importance.
Reptiles, probably Common Lizards or Slow-worms, are also frequent

Table 4.2 *Composition of Kestrels' diets in different zones in Europe*

	Britain and Scandinavia (A)	**West and Central Europe** (B)	**Mediterranean Europe** (C)
Total items	8777	12606	7168
Total vertebrates	4915	11663	995
Voles as a percentage of vertebrates	45	84	15
Mice and rats as a percentage of vertebrates	10	4	23
Shrews as a percentage of vertebrates	11	2	23
Other and unidentified mammals as a percentage of vertebrates	9	1	15
Birds as a percentage of vertebrates	22	8	11
Amphibians and reptiles as a percentage of vertebrates	3	1	13
Invertebrates as a percentage of total items	44	7	86

Sources: (A) Ellis 1946; Cramp and Simmons 1979; Korpimäki 1985b; Yalden and Warburton 1979; Shrubb
1980 and unpublished. (B) Cavé 1968; Cramp and Simmons 1979; Thiollay 1963 and 1968a. (C) Lovari 1974;
Thiollay 1968 a and b.

Adult male Kestrel attacking Starling. It missed by a fraction of a second.

prey in Wales, where every batch of pellets that I have examined in the summer showed varying amounts of scale, indicating that reptiles had been taken.

There are also marked geographical variations in the insect prey of Kestrels. Table 4.1 shows that orthoptera were most important in southern Europe and coleoptera in the north. In the north, orthoptera are taken mainly in late summer and autumn and may thus be under-recorded in the table, as the Finnish and some of the French studies were done in the breeding season. Nevertheless, the Camargue and Corsican samples were also for the breeding season, confirming that these insects are readily available over a longer period in the warmer south.

The bird prey recorded on the nest record cards in Britain also showed an interesting geographic split. Starlings were widely taken, but half of all the seed-eating passerines were recorded from eastern England and virtually all the thrushes and Meadow Pipits from northern England and Scotland. Similarly, all the Moles recorded in this sample were noted from northern England or Scotland, with 70 per cent from northern Scotland.

Seasonal variations in diet

Studies over an extended period in one area have revealed marked seasonal variations in the Kestrel's prey. Thus, in Sussex, bird prey peaked during November–January and in June–July, mammal prey in spring and autumn, and reptiles, mainly Slow-worms or lizards, in spring. Insect prey were taken especially in autumn, as they were in Yalden and Warburton's (1979) study, and earthworms were most frequent during January to March,

44

particularly March. These variations occurred in all three years that I examined prey in detail, and similar ones are clear in other long-term studies

Such variations again seem to reflect mainly the availability of different prey. The tendency to take more birds when easily caught juveniles are available has already been noted. In addition, in my Sussex area an influx of passerines, mainly Skylarks, Starlings and finches, which is characteristic of farmland habitats in winter (Murton 1971), was associated with the winter peak in bird kills. Earthworms peaked in March off newly cultivated fields. In farmland, however, the availability of food for birds often reflects accessibility as well as abundance. For Kestrels suitable small birds were not only more numerous on my study area in winter, they were also easier to catch then than in spring because they could be stalked in areas such as stockyards, where sparrows and Starlings particularly concentrated to feed. These provided good ambush sites for Kestrels. In urban habitats birdtables provide the same facility. In spring, these targets were no longer available on my site as stock were turned out to graze. Similarly, a sharp increase in mammal prey in July coincided with the start of the cereal harvest, making much fresh hunting terrain available. It was also during and after harvest, as cereal stubbles were cleared, that ground beetles figured most prominently in the diet.

Female Kestrel gliding in to attack bird prey in a typical fast, low contour-hugging approach (see page 53).

Marked seasonal variations also occurred in the mammal species taken in my study area. These variations fit well with seasonal changes in the activity of the mammals concerned. Bank Voles, Wood Mice and Harvest Mice were primarily winter prey being less strictly nocturnal then than in summer, rats were most vulnerable to Kestrels (and Barn Owls) when moving to and from fields in spring and autumn (when 74% of them were caught), and Common Shrews were primarily summer prey, being most active on the surface then (Corbet and Southern 1977). Both the number and the proportion of voles in the diet increased in spring, when there was a significant increase in the total proportion of mammals taken. Despite this, I found little increase in hunting activity in the habitats most usually hunted for them (Table 4.3, page 53). In the Netherlands, Masman *et al.* (1988) found that a similar seasonal increase in Common Voles taken reflected an increase in successful strikes at prey, not more hunting activity. Both these points indicate that changes in voles' behaviour in spring increase their vulnerability to Kestrels, and, in south-west Finland, Korpimäki (1985a, b) found that male voles were then caught significantly more frequently than females because they were more active. He also found marked seasonal variations in diet related to snow-melt (which flushes small mammals to the surface) and vegetation growth.

Habitat-related variations

Apart from differences arising from the geographic distribution of prey animals, there are more definitely habitat-related variations in the food of Kestrels in Britain. For example, urban Kestrels probably take a high proportion of birds. This was measured in Manchester by Yalden (1980), who found that birds, probably mainly sparrows, provided 63 per cent of the diet by number and 76 per cent by weight; House Mice and rats were the most important mammal prey. Urban areas probably provide rewarding ambush sites for Kestrels hunting birds, particularly at birdtables and feeders. This pattern, however, is at marked variance with continental records. Studies in Paris and Munich, for example, have shown that Common Voles remain the most important prey (Thiollay 1968; Cramp and Simmons 1979).

Table 4.1 shows sharp differences in the insect species taken between areas of largely pastoral and largely arable farmland in England. In the Lake District, largely devoted to sheep farming, dor beetles (which feed on sheep dung) and caterpillars were the most frequent items. In Sussex ground beetles, very largely taken from cereal fields and stubbles, where they are very numerous, were far more important and dor beetles scarce; the numbers of farmstock kept were small. Dor beetles are also an important item of diet in Wales (Davis 1975), again in an area devoted to sheep.

Wood Mice are common in cultivated fields in Britain and often taken by Kestrels there, but figure rarely in the diet of upland birds. They are scarce in Kestrel diets in Europe as well, and are presumably important in lowland Britain because they partly replace Common Voles in cultivation there. In my Sussex area, Harvest Mice comprised 7 per cent of identified mammal prey. This unusually high percentage reflected the amount of clover grown, which, at 6 per cent of arable land, was very high by British standards in the late 1970s. Harvest Mice were common in these fields, particularly if we left the crop until October for seed. I saw Kestrels take them there regularly.

Individual variations

In my Sussex area, I collected pellets from Kestrel roosts daily whenever possible and analysed each daily batch separately. I checked regularly the sex of birds using roosts. This enabled me to gain insight into the diets of indiv-idual Kestrels on four territories outside the breeding season. About 40 per cent of the pellets collected from these territories then could be assigned to male or female and their diets compared. I found that males took more insect prey (41 per cent of items compared with 18 per cent for females) and females took earthworms more often (46 per cent of pellets contained

Adult male with lizard prey. Lizards are frequent prey in the Welsh uplands and in Sussex farmland.

significant quantities of sand, indicating that earthworms had been eaten, compared with 18 per cent for males). Bird prey is very difficult to identify accurately from pellets: the most frequent evidence was palatal thickenings of seed-eaters' bills. These showed that male Kestrels in my sample took more seed-eaters than females (55 per cent of bird items compared with 36 per cent). In one pair I watched closely, the male took over twice as many birds as the female, but, if reptiles were taken, it was invariably by the female. The samples, both of Kestrels and of prey, in this analysis were quite small and not all differences were statistically significant, although marked. These results are thus tentative and need testing, but Village (1990) also noted some differences between the sexes. They also fit well with my observations of differences in hunting behaviour between the sexes (see below).

Perhaps the most marked variation, however, is that insect prey are particularly important for juvenile Kestrels. In their development of hunting, they start by taking insects, particularly ground beetles, and evidence from pellets and observations of hunting have shown that such prey remains important throughout their first autumn. My observations in Wales support this and in hill country groups of young birds spread out along a ridge and dropping to take small items is a characteristic sight in autumn.

Hunting

The hunting behaviour of the Kestrel is as varied as its food, and the classic perception of hovering and pouncing is only part of the story. In several studies, around half of recorded hunting was from a perch (still-hunting), and Kestrels also search for prey by cruise-hunting or soaring, hawk flying insects, hunt on foot, scavenge and pirate food from other predators.

In the 'Notes' section of *British Birds*, many records of unusual hunting concern Kestrels exploiting farming operations. This, however, was a regular feature of their hunting behaviour in farmland in Sussex. In such lowland farmland, Kestrels follow cultivations to gather earthworms or wait-on at such operations to catch the small mammals they flush. Similarly, they quickly exploit the opportunities provided by cutting grass or cereals or making hay, where the sudden clearance or disturbance of thick cover leaves many prey temporarily highly vulnerable. This is a habit common to many birds in farmland. Kestrels will spend long periods lurking around a machine if the hunting is good: while mowing seed clover, my brother once watched one take eight Harvest Mice flushed by the machine in an afternoon. Long ago, Stevenson (1866) recorded as regular the habit of waiting-on around cornricks in Norfolk to catch the mice flushed by winter threshing. I also observed this habit on my Sussex farm in the 1950s, noting that Harvest Mice were perhaps the most frequent victims. I also noted that Kestrels, like gulls and Rooks, would often check around tractors whatever they were doing, leaving if no hunting chances were offered. Such exploitation of human activity is undoubtedly regular behaviour in farmland, and I believe that it is an important source of successful hunting chances.

Kestrels also hunt on foot quite frequently. I have at least ten records of them trotting about on the ground picking up small prey, mainly beetles, usually after a successful sally from a perch or hover. The bird stands and looks around, trotting forward to take several more items before taking off. The whole performance is remarkably plover-like, and it is a habit that Kestrels share with Buzzards. Kestrels also sometimes hunt small mammals on foot. I once watched a male standing, peering and listening on a ditch bank; it hopped into the headland furrow and trotted along a few metres, then jumped on to a clod to stand, look and listen again. It worked 100 m of the bank like this before jumping feet-first into a tussock of grass and emerging with a shrew. It appeared to work as much by sound as by sight.

Kestrels have also been recorded snatching fish from the surface of ponds or reservoirs, hunting bats and attending Starling roosts. Pairs may hunt co-operatively, but such instances are rare and may be confined to certain types of prey or circumstances. Simms (1977) recorded a pair successfully taking a bat, the male pursuing and the female stooping, and successful hunting of Starlings at roosts may depend on co-operative action or on several Kestrels being present at the same time. Cade (1982) noted that some falcons, such as the Laggar, which seem indifferent performers alone, may be much more efficient co-operative hunters.

Although small birds may provide much of the food taken in farmland, very few hunts of birds by Kestrels conform to the classic perception of hover and pounce. Paradoxically, those that do tend to be the unusual. One of the neatest I have ever seen involved a male Kestrel at Minsmere, Suffolk, which was hovering high over a migrating stream of hirundines and from time to time gently dropping on one to carry it off; he was very successful, too.

All such records underline the Kestrel's versatility as a hunter and the fascination of watching it. Many are almost certainly individual tactics, learned by particular birds to take advantage of local opportunities. Although such tactics may be a fairly regular part of any Kestrel's hunting repertoire, however, the important basic methods of finding prey are from a hover, from a perch or, to a lesser extent, by cruising or soaring.

Search: hover- and still-hunting

The extent to which Kestrels hunt in flight or from a perch varies seasonally in Europe (e.g., Masman *et al.* 1988; Shrubb 1980; Village 1983a)Basically they hover-hunt more in summer and still-hunt more in winter. Local conditions will vary that pattern. Thus hover-hunting was much more frequent in my Welsh area (pastoral and upland) than in my Sussex area (mixed/arable farmland) at all times of the year. Welsh birds still-hunt comparatively rarely because good hunting perches are scarce in the areas most often hunted; nevertheless, still-hunting remains more frequent in winter. R.J. Sandison (pers. comm.) found a similar pattern in an area of open downland; again perches were few. In hill country, Kestrels consistently use the upcurrents on the windward slope of ridges and may hover or hang there for long periods with little effort. They tend to shift hunting sites with wind changes, to take advantage of lift. In all habitats Kestrels hover head to wind. Rijnsdorp *et al.* (1981) found, in the Netherlands, that both calm conditions and strong winds reduced the frequency of hover-hunting. In hill country, however, Kestrels behave rather differently, hover-hunting regardless of wind conditions in summer and more frequently in stronger winds in winter, when increased lift would reduce energy demands (Village 1983a). Calm conditions were rare in my Sussex area, which was coastal, but there I thought that strong winds caused Kestrels to hover lower; my experience in Wales agrees with Village's findings. In fog or rain Kestrels avoid flying as much as possible, and in very rough conditions they will retire to shelter and sit it out, especially in winter.

The heights at which Kestrels hover-hunt also show marked seasonal and regional variations. My Sussex study area was a flat plain festooned with electricity cables carried on ppoles 8–12 m tall. I used these to estimate hovering heights. Broadly, birds hover higher in summer, when vegetation is generally higher and denser, or over more densely vegetated habitats. In Sussex the pattern basically corresponded with the growth and clearance of crops. This was sharply illustrated during haying, when the birds hovered high (over 24 m) over unmown fields, dropping to the normal height band (8–24 m) after the same field was cut. I observed a similar seasonal tendency to over higher in summer in Wales but there Kestrels generally worked higher at all seasons because 63 per cent of all hunting recorded was over rather thick cover, young forestry, dense rough grass and rushes, bracken or scrub, a higher proportion than in Sussex.

Kestrels also constantly vary their height during spells of hover-hunting. A common pattern is to search at one height and to drop when possible prey is detected, swinging back up if no chance offers. They will also persistently work an area at one height and again swing up for a more general search if no prey are found, often moving to another spot and repeating the pattern.

Height clearly broadens the area searched. The dense cover over which Kestrels often hunt is rarely as thick and uniform as it appears to the observer on the ground. Areas of rushes, young forestry and scrubby hillsides usually have a scatter of open patches among them and height enables Kestrels to examine more of these from one position. They also hunt particularly along edges. Except for grass and clover, crops tend to be much more uniform and Kestrels work them only in the early growth stages.

The time for which Kestrels hover over one spot also varies widely, but over 80 per cent of all hovers timed fell in the range often to forty seconds. Hovering times averaged significantly longer in Sussex than in Wales and averaged longer for all adult males than for all brown-tailed birds; known females were tested separately and the same result obtained. These brown-tails are either immature or female, and the difference perhaps arises because of inexperience (immatures) or small differences in wing-loadings (females: see page 13). I found no difference in the frequency with which males, females or immatures hovered or still-hunted, nor in the height at which they worked, except that juveniles tended to hover lower than adults in their early hunting forays. The shorter hovering times noted in Wales seem inexplicable in hunting terms (but see page 75).

It is often difficult to be certain whether a perched bird is hunting or not. Actively hunting birds change perches regularly (every five to seven minutes in Sussex) and strike at prey, but Kestrels hunting small birds from perches are often more passive. In Sussex, searching was in many cases unnecessary: the Kestrel knew, from experience, where small birds were likely to gather, in stockyards or by grain stores for example, and simply sat waiting for a chance; if none was offered it departed quietly elsewhere. A Kestrel might do this for up to half an hour before suddenly striking. If successful this is a very efficient form of hunting, but it looks opportunistic. Nevertheless, if the perch overlooks a spot where Kestrels regularly take prey such tactics are probably deliberate hunting.

My Sussex Kestrels had several favoured perches which were regularly used in this way, sited to look along ditches and hedges or to overlook gardens and buildings, all fruitful sources of prey. The most common perches were telegraph poles and electricity poles and cables, which probably provided an ideal hunting height. They also used buildings and trees and occasionally bushes, hedgerows and fence posts, but the latter are too low for successful searching. Power cables across fields were ideal for hunting earthworms and other invertebrates, and Kestrels often 'leapfrogged' along the line, working from alternate poles. When taking earthworms they worked back and forth along these lines, crossing the same fields several times.

Cruise-hunting and hawking

Cruise-hunting means just that: the Kestrels cruise slowly along, continually looking at fresh ground rather than hovering over one spot. About 4 per cent of hunting in Sussex and 7 per cent in Wales was by such cruising or by hawking flying insects. In Sussex 75 per cent of this hunting was by adult males, and their greater tendency to hawk flying insects probably

Kestrel hover-hunting (see pages 49 et seq.). This brown-headed bird appears to be an immature from the very neat plumage.

partly explains the greater proportion of insects in the male's diet (see page 46). In Wales, however, males and females used these methods equally frequently. There are seasonal variations, too. Cruise-hunting was most frequent during April to July in Sussex and, in both areas, hawking flying insects was particularly an autumn activity (72 per cent of such records).

Most cruise-hunting that I have seen is used to hunt birds. Kestrels work high and drift along apparently aimlessly, often pausing briefly to check before drifting on. If the observer knows the country, it is often obvious that the bird is quietly checking a series of likely target areas. One winter, in Sussex, a male used to do this regularly after we had fed our cattle, checking each stockyard behind us, for these were then prime attractions for small birds, which scavenged in the cattle troughs; in summer the falcons stalked gardens, farmyards, and around grain stores. Often they will drift up to a likely spot and wait-on in a high hover. Height is clearly an effective ambush: I have several times been able to watch both predator and prey closely, and it was clear that the latter never saw the former until too late, or almost so. One Starling survived by letting go and falling off the roof upon which it was sitting as a Kestrel swooped in. Much the same technique was used to take Lapwing chicks, the Kestrel drifting around nesting fields high and slowly, while the adult Lapwings laboured up to drive them off; if the Kestrels spotted a chick before the adults reached them to drive them off, they dived, grabbed the chick and were off without pause, often with a posse of adult Lapwings in vain pursuit. This seems to be the common way such prey is taken, and Kestrels can cause severe problems around sites such as terneries as their technique is difficult for species which defend their young by mobbing action to combat.

In Britain, Kestrels look for opportunities to hawk flying insects by searching airspace below them in a high hovering stance or by looking up from a perch. Sometimes they are attracted by similarly engaged Starlings and Black-headed Gulls. Prey is usually taken in the feet, the action graceful and easy like that of Hobbies, and Kestrels may take such prey over distances of 200–300 m. They also take flying insects in the bill, working like Black-headed Gulls. Possibly these Kestrels are mainly juveniles.

Table 4.3 *Habitats in which prey of each class were taken or attacked in farmland in Sussex. Percentages are of total attacks at each prey in descending order of frequency.*

BIRDS		MAMMALS		INVERTEBRATES	
Habitat	Percentage of total attacks	Habitat	Percentage of total attacks	Habitat	Percentage of total attacks
Vicinity of buildings/ gardens	29	Field boundaries roads, tracks	25	Young cereals	41
Field boundaries roads, tracks	28	Clover leys	21	Stubbles	27
Clover leys	14	Stubbles	21	Clover leys	12
Stubbles	14	Rough grass	12	Ploughed or new sown ground	10
Other crops	11	Other crops	12	Field boundaries roads, tracks	6
Young cereals	4	Vicinity of buildings/ gardens	5	Other crops	3
		Ploughed, new sown ground, young cereals	4	Rough grass	1

Striking and seizing prey

Where a Kestrel appears to be searching is often not where it is actually hunting. In hill country a Kestrel may strike well downslope of its apparent position: in farmland the species often stalks prey from a distance. Furthermore, open hills, meadows or fields may be mosaics of short and tall vegetation: which the Kestrel is watching can be known only if it strikes.

Hunting effort in Sussex and in Wales was fairly evenly divided between well-vegetated sites and those with well-cropped or sparse herbage. As a rule, Kestrels tend to take vertebrates from the former and invertebrates from the latter, but I doubt if it is safe to draw firm conclusions from this. Table 4.3 shows the habitats in which different prey classes were attacked in Sussex; many invertebrates were taken from well-vegetated habitats such as clover leys. It also shows the importance in farmland of minority areas of permanent habitat such as field boundaries, or crops standing through the year such as clover. These provided 24 per cent of the terrain, but 70 per cent of chances at birds and 60 per cent of those at mammals. Field boundaries are particularly valuable for, although limited in area, they are linear and thus distributed through the landscape. Hunting Kestrels can be watched following the line of a hedge or ditch through a series of fields.

In both Sussex and Wales, I separated strikes by known males and females outside the breeding season and found significant differences. These are presumably linked to the differences in the prey taken by the sexes.

Much straightforward hover-hunting is probably for small mammals. When such prey are detected the Kestrel usually comes down in stages, checking its position and the target before making the final plunge from 3–6 m or so (a stepped strike). The strike is made with the feet, which are swung forward just before impact. Often, however, the Kestrel breaks off before impact and swings back up again. It may leave the spot, hover elsewhere and slip back after a few minutes for another check; I have seen birds do this two or three times before striking or giving up and leaving. This procedure may be varied by Kestrels making plummeting dives to strike direct at the ground, sometimes from considerable height (direct stoops). From watching hunting I have concluded that Kestrels often cannot see their target very clearly, working on brief glimpses and perhaps by interpreting movements in cover and/or partly by sound. Similar considerations apply to still-hunting and explain the otherwise oddly low success rates against mammals, which various studies (summarized by Village 1990) put at 9–56 per cent. Direct stoops are probably at targets that give a clear view and my impression is that these are often more successful than stepped strikes, but I have not quantified it. Certainly, however, Kestrels very rarely miss a small mammal stranded away from cover by agricultural operations.

Strikes at birds are quite distinct. From a perch (sometimes a low hover) Kestrels characteristically attack in a very low fast dash, with the flight surfaces closed right up, giving a very Merlin-like appearance. They take advantage of any cover such as a fold in the ground, stubble, ditches, trees, hedges or buildings to ensure surprise. Often the target has a restricted line of escape, among buildings or by walls, fences or garden hedges, a ploy which may work against the Kestrel for, in a cold spell, I once watched a sickly Redwing elude pursuit by dashing down 100 m of barbed-wire fence, dodging in and out of the strands before diving to cover. These attacks are invariably made over a distance. I measured 29 instances in Sussex, which ranged from 70 to 630 m and averaged 280. Kestrels use this distance to generate the speed and power needed to stop a bird (see page 14). Birds are usually taken on the ground but may be grabbed off buildings or taken in bushes and hedges, into which Kestrels will crash out of sight with considerable force. Kestrels also hunt birds by the cruise/high-hover technique described above, attacking in a full stoop or a powered dive in which diving speed is increased by short flicking wingbeats. Many attacks at birds by Kestrels look fairly suicidal, but I have no record of one injuring itself.

Village (1990) suggested that Kestrels find birds difficult to catch. Certainly they are not aerodynamically well adapted to catch flying birds, but I think that this observation needs modifying. Where Kestrels can take birds by surprise or at a disadvantage they are highly successful (see page 58), and farmland, suburban and urban habitats offer many such chances of ambush. In more open landscapes they are probably less successful, and Village, for his arable farmland site, suggested that Kestrels took birds mainly at dusk, which again provided an ambush situation.

A curious aspect of the Kestrel's hunting of birds is 'boo' flights. In these it flies at a party of birds (occasionally singles) feeding on the ground and flushes them, often circling them, before quietly moving away. These do not seem to be serious attempts to kill: the Kestrel makes no attempt at concealment and is flying too slowly for success, although it may finish with a swoop and flourish. It looks as if it is stirring the flock up to look it over and this may be the behaviour's function. Such flights are possibly largely by immatures learning to hunt, although I have seen adults perform them. They bear an interesting similarity to the 'low-intensity' hunting by

Male Kestrel attacking birds, the target by a fence which often gives the predator a marginal advantage.

Peregrines described by Ratcliffe (1980). It is also remarkable how infrequently common target species such as Starlings take any notice of Kestrels.

Invertebrates are caught mainly by rather different techniques. In my experience, earthworms are invariably taken from a perch, either when working at the surface or when exposed by farmwork. Kestrels may detect them over considerable distances – at 80 m in one instance. They pull them up with the bill but are also recorded scratching for them (something I have not seen). Insect prey are also captured on the ground, as well as on the wing. In many cases the mode of taking them – coming down gently, often picking them up with the bill, eating them *in situ* or as the Kestrel rises – is characteristic, as is catching them in short vegetation. These are not, however, entirely reliable distinctions and I have found in Wales particularly that I often cannot tell what a Kestrel is hunting unless I can identify a kill.

Management of a hunting range

In Britain and Europe, at least, Kestrels usually hunt singly. Even if families or other assemblies are hunting together, as they will in autumn in the hills, they maintain a spacing of 50 m or so. In Sussex such behaviour was unusual, and even family parties spread out to hunt, with birds 200 m or so apart. Such group hunting is, in my experience, always for insects, but I have not seen what occurs during vole plagues. Otherwise, even when numerous, Kestrels hunt very widely spaced and territorial behaviour reinforces this.

Where hunting ranges overlap there is a marked tendency for birds to hunt alternately. I found this easy to see during farmwork such as haying, when I could watch males coming from different sites. Aggression usually resulted if two males coincided, and this may have governed the pattern, but perhaps each male was more usually aware of what the other was doing. Village (1990) noted very similar behaviour in Scottish uplands.

Experienced adults know their ranges and the opportunities they afford, visiting a fruitful site daily, often at the same time, until it ceases to be worthwhile. When feeding young, males often use the same site all day if successful. This behaviour was studied in the Netherlands by Rijnsdorp *et al.* (1981), who found a statistical probability that birds would return to a site where successful 24 hours before: they also found that they could influence a Kestrel's behaviour by offering it food at a regular time and place.

Outside the breeding season, hunting ranges may be occupied by a single bird or shared by a pair that has remained together. In the autumn juveniles share their parents' territories until dispersal. When a range is shared, males and females tend to work different parts, different habitats or the same areas at different times, a point discussed further in the next chapter.

Kestrels often also hunt in one place in the morning and another in the afternoon: daily collection and analysis of pellets from roosts underlines this. My Sussex Kestrels took a mixture of birds and mammals on 27 per cent of days, a mixture of mammals on a further 12 per cent and a mix of vertebrates and invertebrates on a further 13 per cent. These needed different techniques and tended to be taken from different places (Table 4.3), so the birds were using a range of hunting methods and sites regularly.

Timing of hunting

For a complete year in Sussex, I logged the time (as GMT) for every Kestrel I saw hunting. Although the records are biased by my own work routine (the midday break shown represents the observer's main feeding period!) and are unsuitable for statistical analysis, nevertheless they can be used for simple comparisons. They are plotted in Figure 4.1. The main point shown is that hunting activity at both seasons exhibited several of peaks during the day. The highest level of activity often tended to be in the mornings, although many times I specifically remarked on a lack of activity very early. However, I had few records for the dawn period in summer. In winter and spring, there seemed to be a strong tendency to hunt at each end of the day.

This subject was examined in greater detail by Rijnsdorp *et al.* (1981) and Raptor Group RUG/RIJP (1982) in the Netherlands. They found a rhythm of peak activity by Kestrels roughly every two hours during three February days of intensive watching and that these peaks coincided with peaks in surface activity by voles. The circumstances of this study were unusual, but it seems very probable that such behaviour is broadly general among Kestrels. It will be considerably modified, however, where they regularly take a wider spectrum of prey than recorded in the Dutch study.

Kestrels may also adjust their hunting times by caching prey and retrieving it to eat later. Such behaviour can be difficult to observe systematically unless Kestrels can be followed for long periods, and it has not been quantified in detail in Britain, but the same Dutch workers found that some prey were regularly cached, sometimes partly eaten, and retrieved and eaten most frequently in the last two hours before dusk. This habit was much less marked in summer than in winter. Such behaviour clearly separates the function of hunting from that of eating, and has marked

Kestrel caching prey (here Wood Mice). Cache sites are often on the ground behind trees or bushes, etc.

advantages if the birds can concentrate on hunting at optimum times and eat later. Rijnsdorp *et al.* (1981) found that cached prey accounted for a maximum of 79 per cent of meals in the last two hours of the day in late winter but none in August and September. Caching thus helped to ensure a meal before roosting, which may be particularly important in winter.

At nests, I noted that males bring more food than the female immediately requires and regularly store it. The female then collects food from this larder when she needs it. I have also seen males take food to eat from such stores and have seen one apparently discard it. Such behaviour presumably accounts for the sharp morning peaks apparent in my hunting records in the breeding season (Figure 4.1). At nests, larders may be on the ground behind stumps or tree trunks, on tree stumps or on sites such as metal cross-bars of electricity poles. Village (1990) noted other favourite sites as grass tussocks, clods of earth or behind fence posts. Cached prey is rarely buried or covered, although it is sometimes tucked into a crevice.

Kestrels are also at times decidedly crepuscular in their hunting in Britain and have once been recorded hunting by moonlight (Roberts 1946); I have often wondered if the latter may not be more frequent. Regular taking of prey such as Wood Mice must involve Kestrels hunting at dawn and dusk. It is not unusual to see them active up to half an hour after sunset, and I have noted them hunting when it is too dark to read outside. Such behaviour is likely to be underrecorded because it is difficult to observe.

Figure 4.1 *Timing of hunting by Kestrels during a year in Sussex farmland.*

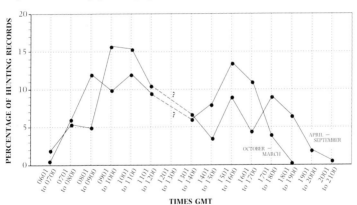

Hunting performance

Recording hunting success of Kestrels can be surprisingly difficult. It is best done from cover, otherwise Kestrels tend to watch you watching them, and they have a highly developed facility for vanishing if you turn your head away. Further problems arise in determining when a bird is hunting, at least from a perch. Inevitably this is partly a subjective decision by the observer. The wide variations in the success of still-hunting birds recorded in published studies presumably reflect this. Daily collection and analysis of pellets also show clearly that farmland Kestrels in Britain, at least, have a strong tendency to take a variety of prey, needing varied techniques, daily. I have watched a Kestrel hover-hunt unsuccessfully for an hour, retire to a perch and within three minutes grab a Blackbird. Such observations give a rather different perspective to hunting success from that obtained by building up success rates from a series of samples of hovering or still-hunting birds, which may not relate very clearly to the birds' actual daily routines. In the Netherlands, however, Masman *et al.* (1988) followed Kestrels for whole days and recorded their activity. Overall, they found that their Kestrels caught between three and four voles per hour of flight-hunting (hover-hunting), with a seasonal variation of about two in January to six in July, the latter when feeding young. The birds were more successful in summer mainly because they caught more of what they struck at, so prey was more accessible. Still-hunting individuals caught from 0.3 voles per hour in winter to 0.1 in summer, this seasonal difference reflecting the probability that perched birds in summer were more likely to be resting than hunting. These results suggest that these Kestrels could obtain their daily requirements from about two hours' flight-hunting in winter and two to three in summer. This would not be continuous activity. I found that Kestrels rested during bouts of hover-hunting, and males often rested for ten minutes or so after visits to nests, so that an hour of hover-hunting would be spread over two hours or so of daytime. In practice, the Dutch birds obtained about 24 per cent of their food by an average of about 4.5 hours' still-hunting daily in winter, obtaining the rest by an average of just over an hour's flight-hunting. Altogether, these results indicated that these Kestrels used about five to seven hours of daytime for hunting to gather their daily requirements.

The Dutch birds fed very largely on voles, and so these findings may not be directly applicable to Kestrels taking a wider range of prey. There must be much variation. In Sussex, Kestrels regularly hunted earthworms daily in late winter and early spring and took other invertebrates which, my impression was, were often deliberately sought. Timing a succession of hover- and still-hunting individuals suggested that, with the mixed diet taken, there was little difference in success rates between hunting modes, each yielding about four or five items an hour. I could not, however, estimate true hunting yields because I was often uncertain just what prey had been taken.

My Kestrels also took nearly as many birds as mammals in winter. The birds averaged twice the weight of the mammals caught, although this does not necessarily translate directly into a difference in nutritional value. No study has really got to grips with the energetics of bird-hunting by Kestrels, but the techniques I noted regularly looked more energy-efficient than hover-hunting for mammals. They were also successful in terms of the ratio of bird kills to strikes: of 95 strikes at birds (in Sussex), 27 (28 per cent) were successful (the number of strikes includes 'boo' flights, so the success rate is probably understated). Judging from the figures given by Village (1990), this is not an exceptional success rate for Kestrels hunting birds. My Kestrels were more successful in attacks at bird prey around buildings than at field boundaries or field habitats, but the methods of attack – stoop from a height or fast low dash – were equally successful.

A marked disparity between high yields for hover-hunting and low ones for still-hunting is common to all studies of Kestrels' hunting that I have examined. Why does this species vary its hunting method seasonally, using the least productive way in winter? Although the pattern is influenced by seasonal variations in prey, weather, and by the seasonal growth of vegetation forcing birds to work higher in summer, there seem to be two main reasons. First, hunting and territorial marking from a perch (see Chapter 5) may not be easily distinguishable, and the latter is also particularly a winter activity. Thus, the true yield from still-hunting is better than we record, or still-hunting is more efficient as Kestrels combine it with another important function. Second, for self-maintenance Kestrels often need to do no more, hover-hunting in winter simply to top up. Masman *et al.* (1988) calculated that the mixed pattern of flight- and still-hunting observed in winter in the Netherlands resulted in significant savings in energy: Kestrels could have found their requirements more quickly by hover-hunting, but it was better, in terms of energy gained to energy used, to gather a significant proportion of food by still-hunting. In summer, the increased requirements of a female and brood demanded the the most productive method.

Scavenging

I agree with Ash (1960, 1965), who found that scavenging dead mammals and birds was much more frequent among Kestrels than usually supposed. He noted that some gamekeepers exploited the habit by placing traps by any dead bird they found. Of the fifteen or so records I gathered in three years in Sussex, most were also quarry species – three pigeons, three Pheasants, two rabbits a hare and a partridge. Of the remainder, three

Male Kestrel hawking flying insects. Males are more addicted to this habit than females although both sexes do it.

59

were road casualties (a rat and two Hedgehogs) and one was a gull. I also certainly lost two birds, possibly as many as five, mainly females, in one winter and spring which had been poisoned by baits put out for foxes.

Scavenging was certainly more frequent than my records show. Each winter I found pellets containing large quills or unusual mammal fur and large pieces of bone, which I attributed to scavenging. Their matrix differed markedly from those from normal prey, and twice I found such pellets at a roost the morning after watching the bird using it feeding at a dead Pheasant. Such scavenging could be important at times for individual birds: I estimated that it supplied 28 per cent of one immature Kestrel's food in December 1980 and 32 per cent of an adult male's in February 1981.

Nevertheless I have not seen Kestrels scavenge in Wales, and Village (1990) thought the habit rare, so its frequency is clearly variable. The high proportion of Man's quarry species in the records suggests that scavenging may be particularly frequent where game is preserved and shot. The nest record cards of the BTO, however, included a record of a pair in Perthshire feeding largely on sheep carrion and Kestrels have been recorded eating food put out on birdtables (Bradley 1966, pers. obs.). I have only seen Kestrels dispute carcases with Magpies, and the falcons were dominant. I once watched, with much amusement, a female feeding on a dead Brown Hare, with three Magpies flirting and titupping around her about 6 m away and not daring to go closer; they had to wait for her to finish.

Piracy

Kestrels also pirate food from other predators, usually avian, but the 'Notes' section of *British Birds* included seven or eight records of them robbing or trying to rob Weasels during 1957–79. I have recorded Kestrels successfully robbing Sparrowhawks (two or three times), Barn Owls and Magpies and regularly robbing or trying to rob other Kestrels. Piracy may be more frequent between young birds, but adults steal food from each other and I once watched an adult female dash in beneath her own brood, lift a small mammal from under their noses and depart. While not actually piracy, this was definitely poaching! Such piracy is not always successful, for birds will bounce others if they see them strike, whether successful or not, presumably because the victim is then most vulnerable. Juveniles may try to steal food from others in flight, but otherwise the victim is usually on the ground.

Piracy against Short-eared Owls seems to be the most widely recorded example in the literature, and Village (1990) also found this species to be the most frequent victim in his Scottish study area, noting a 30 per cent success rate by the Kestrels. In Sussex, however, although these owls wintered regularly, I never recorded any interaction between them and Kestrels. Nor did I see Kestrels try to rob harriers, although they often mobbed them. Overall, it is likely that piracy is simple opportunism and makes little real contribution to the important business of obtaining food. Village, however, records one Kestrel apparently living by robbing Short-eared Owls in his Scottish study area in the winter of 1977/8, so it may again be important at times to individuals.

5

HUNTING RANGE, TERRITORY AND DISPLAY

ALTHOUGH the literature often states that Kestrels defend only a small area around the nest as territory, their behaviour in this respect is very variable. Often they defend substantial areas as territory and have a very varied vocabulary of territorial and display flights. The area over which they hunt (hunting range) and the area defended as territory are not necessarily the same, and hunting ranges, if they differ, are larger.

In Sussex, a high proportion of territorial activity always appeared to be directed at maintaining a substantial area of hunting range as exclusive territory. This was particularly marked in June, when males were feeding young in the nest, and in autumn, when juveniles were dispersing. In June males apparently competed for favoured hunting sites, and territorial disputes resulted if they met. Quite often, however, they used such sites alternately. Hover-hunting is a very conspicuous activity and, reinforced by the strongly patterned upperparts of male Kestrels, may serve as a signal which encourages them to alternate and so spaces them out. There was also a marked tendency for the focus of territorial activity to shift from hunting terrain to the vicinity of nest sites in the spring.

In upland Wales, although I have recorded much interaction with other raptors and with corvids, I have noted only sixteen instances of territorial disputes between Kestrels in five years; they are very thinly spread and rarely meet. On his upland site in Scotland, however, where pairs broke up in the autumn, Village (1990) found that Kestrels held individual winter territories, which were also exclusive hunting ranges. These territories also expanded during the winter as birds left or died and neighbours filled gaps. In the breeding season, nest sites, which tended to be clumped in valleys, and their vicinity were defended as territory but the more uniformly and widely distributed hunting terrain was increasingly shared. Nevertheless, males spaced themselves out when hunting the same area, either by hunting at different times (alternating) or by interactions if two males came together.

As in other studies of farmland Kestrels, my farmland territories appeared to be rather stable throughout the year because pairs often remained together during the winter and then maintained them (but see page 68). Although both birds of the pair defended the shared territory, they almost invariably hunted separately. If they hunted the same area they did so at different times, but there was a strong tendency for the sexes to hunt different parts of the territory or range. I examined this in detail for one November to January period, when the population was particularly stable, simply dividing the area into four blocks and plotting the frequency of hunting by males and females in each. There were more records of males, but this exercise showed that females hunted in the southern half of the area proportionately much more often and the difference was statistically significant. The crops grown and the rotations on the six farms concerned differed, so this tendency to hunt separate parts also reinforced the tendency for males and females to take prey from different habitats (page 52). Thus, these birds separated themselves for hunting either in time or by space or by using different habitats. Hunting at different times may lead to some separation in prey, as does using different habitats. Village (1990) noted a similar tendency for the sexes to divide a shared territory between them on his farmland sites.

Other variations in the extent of territorial behaviour occur. Cavé (1968), working in the Dutch polders, found that Kestrels established and maintained exclusive hunting territories in winter only if food was short but not otherwise; in summer, only the vicinity of nest sites was defended. Elsewhere, colonial or semi-colonial breeding has been recorded quite widely (e.g., Fennel 1954; Ferguson-Lees 1972; Village 1990), and Newton (1979) noted that such instances always occurred in areas with abundant food and limited nest sites. The apparent difference in territorial behaviour among winter visitors to Africa and India has been noted (page 21).

Clearly, the range of territorial behaviour in Kestrel populations relates either to food supply or to nest sites. Where food is abundant and hunting terrain uniformly distributed, territorial defence is likely to be focused on nest sites. Even if the hunting range is not strictly defended, however, there is a marked tendency for hunting males to separate themselves over the shared range. Territorial activity maintaining some exclusive hunting range occurs increasingly where food is more restricted, for example in winter in Europe or in farmland; good hunting sites may actually be the scarce resource in the latter.

Size of hunting ranges

Hunting ranges vary very widely in size in different habitats, and annually and seasonally in the same habitat. Table 5.1 gives the size of hunting range calculated in several different habitats in Britain. I only estimated range sizes in the breeding season, by plotting traffic to and from nests. The size of ranges partly reflects the number of Kestrels present. Ranges will expand if gaps appear in the system and contract if newcomers succeed in creating additional territories.

Lowland farmland in England attracts quite substantial numbers of Kestrels as winter visitors (Chapter 9). Village noted these as more numerous on arable than on his mixed farmland, and county bird reports and ringing returns clearly indicate an influx particularly into arable eastern England. These winter visitors carve territories for themselves within the existing framework of local birds, so winter territories tend to be smaller than summer ones. In one autumn I watched this process closely by a young Kestrel which used my house as a roost. This bird hunted an area which straddled the boundary between two existing territories. Such points are presumably the weakest in an existing system. This winter influx is interesting because winter visitors are actually capitalizing on a favourable change in resources. In any given area of arable farmland the food resources available to Kestrels are probably greater in winter than in summer. There is often an influx of small birds and there is much more huntable terrain, as ground is either bare of crops or they are only just established, so important prey, such as Wood Mice or earthworms, are much more readily caught. Much of this ground ceases to be suitable hunting terrain as crops grow, which restricts the breeding population and must contribute to the greater size of summer ranges.

Other habitat factors may influence the size of area Kestrels need in farmland. Field size affects the amount of field boundary, an important hunting site (Table 4.3), available; areas of large fields have proportionately less. Crop rotations may be significant. One-year clover leys were favoured hunting areas for my Sussex Kestrels but their distribution changed annually with crop rotations, varying the area freely available to any pair; the presence of the crop, however, probably contributed to the comparatively high density of pairs on the six farms involved.

In Wales, away from extensive open hill, I have found breeding Kestrels to range over large areas, but they actually hunt in much more limited sites within them. Much of the intervening ground comprises closely grazed sheep pastures of no value for hunting in the breeding season, a situation very similar to that obtaining with cereals in arable farmland. In Scotland, Village (1990) found that mean hunting-range size was negatively correlated with the abundance of voles, the main prey. A relationship between prey abundance and the size of area hunted is probably general, but the nature of the hunting habitat is clearly also important.

Table 5.1 *The mean size of hunting ranges, in km^2, worked by Kestrels in different habitats in Britain.*

| Region | Habitat | Mean size (and number) of hunting ranges | | Reference |
		Summer	Winter	
Scotland 1975-78	Sheepwalk, forestry	4.53 (48)	2.92 (22)	Village 1990
Wales 1989-91	Upland farms, forestry	8.00 (3)		Shrubb (pers. obs.)
Rutland 1980-84	Mixed farmland	5.09 (32)	2.97 (36)	Village 1990
Sussex 1979-80	Mixed/arable farmland	3.13 (7)		Shrubb (pers. obs.)
Cambridgeshire 1981-85	Arable farmland	9.01 (12)	2.25 (3)	Village 1990
Cambridgeshire 1977-81	Arable farmland	4.64 (11)		Pettifor 1983

Note: Pettifor's figure is for all the year.

Seasonal variations in
territorial and display behaviour

In Sussex. I examined this behaviour closely during 1978–81. Both males and females joined in territorial defence and display, 89 per cent of my records involving males compared with 42 per cent for females; some concerned both. These proportions remained constant throughout the whole year. I found it difficult to separate courtship or sexual displays clearly from territorial ones because many flights obviously fulfilled both of these functions.

There was a marked seasonal pattern in the frequency of territorial and display behaviour (Figure 5.1). Some activity occurred throughout the year. The three peaks occurred in the early part of the breeding season, when the main concern was attracting or holding a mate or holding a nest site, in June. when males were hunting for young broods (see above), and in September. when young were dispersing through the area or attempting to settle. The trough of activity in midwinter is rather misleading, as Kestrels actually spent much time then sitting on prominent perches marking territory (page 71). In May. during incubation. Kestrels are very

Male Kestrels in territorial dispute over a nest site. The defending bird is below, pushing the intruder up and away.

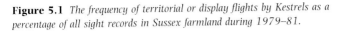

Figure 5.1 *The frequency of territorial or display flights by Kestrels as a percentage of all sight records in Sussex farmland during 1979–81.*

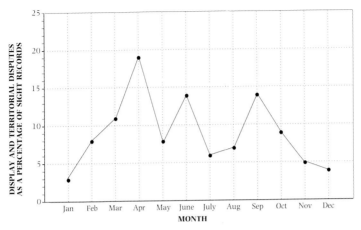

surreptitious, and the June peak of activity died down rapidly in July. The amount of hunting activity certainly decreased by then as demand from fledged broods declined and birds went into heavy moult, but the actual decline in territorial disputes probably also stemmed from the availability of new ground to hunt. We started harvesting cereals in July, clearing much fresh hunting terrain, and there was a marked switch to hunting stubbles during the month. The June outbreak of territorial activity may thus have partly reflected the patchy nature at that time of available hunting resources. The peaks in Figure 5.1 occurred each year, and I found that even settled pairs spent a surprising amount of time probing their neighbours' domains, provoking display. Conspicuous displays also advertised occupation of a site. Displays which seem concerned mainly with courtship and breeding nevertheless also occur outside the breeding season. Some level of courtship display at all times may help to maintain the pair-bond for wintering pairs, which tend to hunt individually in different parts of their range. This is also maintained by the habit pairs have in winter of meeting daily and sitting on favourite perches, preening or simply sitting together; with one pair I noticed this habit particularly in the evening before roosting. I found it a sound guide as to whether a pair was present on a territory.

There were also seasonal differences in the frequency of the main displays which were largely associated with the shift to territorial activity at nest sites in spring. I recorded nine distinct types of display flight (described below). Territorial incidents sometimes included more than one type of display, particularly during February–April, when I recorded some complex performances. 13 per cent of 202 incidents were seen in November–January, 40 per cent in February–April, 18 per cent in May–July and 29 per cent in August–October. That some displays were used mainly in the breeding season does not mean that they were primarily courtship displays. They may have been particularly significant in defending or advertising an occupied nest site.

Circling, soaring and tail-fanning This simple performance was involved in 29 per cent of the incidents I saw. Probably some of these records should be linked with direct territorial attacks (see below), as I first observed the birds at the later stages of a territorial dispute. Nevertheless, 75 per cent of my records for this behaviour as a separate evolution were for the breeding season, a sharply different pattern from the territorial attacks. Males and pairs together often soar and circle over nest sites with much tail-fanning. In males particularly, the latter is a very conspicuous signal and this flight then seems to serve the purposes of courtship and of advertising that a site is held. Otherwise it is definitely a territorial defence. In territorial disputes birds are stacked, with the defending bird almost invariably below. They then circle and soar below the interloper with the tail fanned, displaying the strongly patterned upperparts, occasionally 'shivering' (see below) or even hovering, and steadily pushing the interloper up and away from their territory. Altogether, 81 per cent of the records involved males only and 19 per cent females or pairs.

Shivering This is the winnowing flight of Village (1990). Kestrels fly around rather slowly, with wings held slightly bowed below the line of the body and with rapid shallow wingbeats: the wing does not rise above the body, and often the action looks no more that a rapid vibration or shivering of the wingtip. This seems to be a very generalized flight, occurring uniformly through the seasons and involved in 25 per cent of the incidents I saw. It is used in display between pairs, as a greeting between pairs, in territorial disputes and in response to intrusions at the nest by humans. Flights by males comprised 67 per cent of my records and by females or pairs 33 per cent.

Direct territorial attacks and fighting Of 48 straightforward attacks by one bird upon another, to drive it away from the nest site or hunting territory, 19 per cent ended in physical contact, although this was of very short duration between adults and juveniles. More usually, however, the bird attacked took off, if perched, to avoid contact or, if on the wing, the attacking bird shot underneath it and circled, fanned its tail and sometimes 'shivered' and hovered, as described above, slowly rising and pushing the intruder away. This behaviour often seems partly designed to prevent the other bird from continuing to hunt, and I once watched an adult male jumping about on the ground beneath a poaching juvenile which was working too low for the adult conveniently to circle under. Over 50 per cent of my records of direct attacks were for the period September to November, when young birds were dispersing through the area or seeking to settle there. Males and females took a fairly equal share of such territorial defence, with adult males alone involved in only 58 per cent of the records.

Taken together with circling, soaring and tail-fanning, these flights were much the most frequent forms of territorial dispute that I observed and, unless the strongly patterned upperparts of Kestrels, particularly of males,

Plumage patterns of the upperparts of falcons breeding in Britain compared. The much bolder contrast in the Kestrel is important in territorial behaviour.

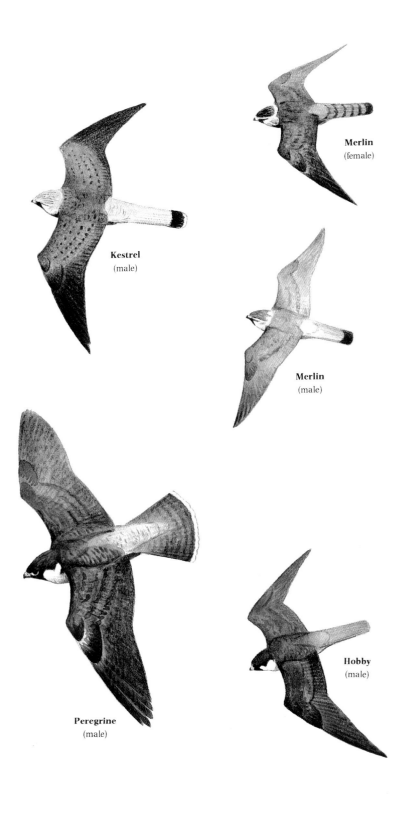

Merlin
(female)

Kestrel
(male)

Merlin
(male)

Peregrine
(male)

Hobby
(male)

are an important and powerful signal in reinforcing territory, it is difficult to explain why they so persistently place themselves in a technically vulnerable position, or why trespassers do not retaliate by diving on them, which I did not see. When Kestrels mob larger raptors, they invariably attack from above.

Although I have occasionally noted more serious fighting between juveniles in autumn, most serious conflicts were between adult males in early spring, and even then they were uncommon. Comparing my experience for 1979–81, with Village's account left the clear impression that he found fighting a much more frequent feature of territorial behaviour in Scotland, where many pairs or individuals resettled the area each spring, and in arable farmland, where an influx of winter visitors occurred each autumn. In the more settled territorial pattern of my farmland area, territory was usually successfully maintained by more ritualized flights. Perhaps, therefore, fighting is symptomatic of more unstable territorial systems. Furthermore, I observed serious fighting between adult males in spring more frequently in Sussex in the mid 1980s, when there were fewer nest sites, (many old elms had been felled) and a 20 per cent increase in cereals area had restricted hunting terrain; primarily, clover was no longer grown. Such fighting is anything but a ritual performance. I once found two males fighting in a tree, one of them hanging upside-down, pinned by its foot to a branch by the other, which was biting it vigorously between intervals of swearing! Fights are noisy and the birds usually grapple each other's talons, flapping and wrestling about on the ground, as well as on tree stumps or hedges for example. With their feet locked they bite with enthusiasm. In 1984, a prolonged war between at least two pairs for possession of a nest site and territory around my house lasted from 15 February to 20 March and ended when I found one male dead, blinded in one eye, with a serious wound on the back of the head and its neck broken. As I did not see this happen, I cannot certainly say that it was murder, but I never doubted that it was.

Rocking flight To a much greater degree than the other main flights listed, I found this to be a male display. I have only two or three records of females doing it. It is also primarily a spring display. It is often, but by no means invariably, performed at considerable height, and displaying birds may cover substantial areas; I once watched one go right around a 20-ha field, a distance surprisingly of nearly 2 km. The flight surfaces are slimmed right down, the wings are held arched or bowed, and the birds fly with a rapid skipping wing action, flicking from side to side like a Snipe. The wing attitude and action lead to the pale underwing catching the light and flashing a conspicuous signal. Kestrels often shoot around their nest areas in this display. They also perform high above nest sites and along territory boundaries. Among variants of this display that I have seen were: a male and female together which soared to a great height above their nest site and then came down at immense speed in a long shallow dive, using the rocking flight action and keeping perfect formation; a male which was rising and falling in a switchback motion, rather than twisting from side to side; and a female which descended in wide sweeping circles, with set wings and flight surfaces tightly slimmed, exactly as though sliding down a spiral staircase. This is clearly an important display and may, as Village remarked, be under-recorded because it is often performed at height. It is undoubtedly used in courtship; males may use it to attract a mate, and I have seen them perform it with great vigour after delivering food to their mates (as well as doing a mild form of the display when bringing food in). I believe, however, that this flight serves mainly to advertise and defend occupied nest sites. Village's (1990) account also showed that his pairs performed together more frequently than I found in Sussex. Again, this may suggest that variations in the display behaviour of Kestrels are related to the stability of territorial systems.

Display stoops Kestrels seem not to have as a common display flight the pattern of dives and upward swoops which regularly features in the displays of accipiters and Buzzards, for example. I have, however, seen male Kestrels do this four times and a female once, so it may occur more often than my records show. Many display performances also end with a magnificent stoop, usually to the nest area but sometimes to territory boundaries. On several occasions I have seen the male arrive by the female and mate.

Such manoeuvres may not really be separate displays, but an important courtship display involves the male repeatedly diving at the female. This is predominantly a spring performance but it is not infrequent in winter, suggesting that pairs may form very early. Sometimes the female is perched and this performance can then look very hostile, as the male shoots past very close, making the female apparently flinch. When very excited, the male may start a regular pendulum pattern, shooting down past her and up between two points, rolling off the top with each turn and plunging down again, a highly spectacular performance. One male varied this by shooting along upside-down. Nevertheless, the classic form of this display is on the wing, the male and female soaring together, male above and continually diving at his mate, passing close to her so that she flicks over on to her side and presents talons. One pair I watched doing this for over half an hour varied the process three times by diving headlong away to their site, keeping perfect station, and then soaring up to repeat the performance. I have seen such co-ordinated formation flying at other times during display by pairs, and it may be a display in its own right. It occurs, too, in other raptors, e.g., Goshawks, and in Ravens. I found such lengthy and dramatic diving displays rather exceptional, however, and quite often the birds simply tilted and darted at one another, although they often appeared to touch talons.

'V'-flight or 'butterfly' Village (1990) noted that this flight often occurred as a finale to a rocking display, the Kestrels, mainly males, dropping rapidly to their site with wings held above the body in an exaggerated 'V'. He also saw birds using it in low-level courtship flights around nests. In Sussex, I saw it used only in the latter circumstances and during territorial arguments. When I analysed my records, I was also surprised to find that I had recorded the flight almost as frequently by females as by males (48 per cent of records to 52 per cent) and that it occurred rather uniformly through the year. Males seemed to use it mainly to attract females to potential nest sites, but females used it in territorial arguments involving the pair, the male perhaps performing a rocking flight to discourage

intruders above the site while the female glided around below in a 'V'-flight. In such circumstances she would look remarkably like a large butterfly or moth. Females did this outside the breeding season if a territorial argument involving the pair included her site, and occasionally they performed this display at territorial boundaries.

Unusual display flights

Besides the above, I recorded some less common displays. The most frequent of these was slow-flighting, the bird flying with slow, deep and exaggerated wingbeats, a performance really remarkably like a displaying Nightjar. Slow-flighting is a common display by accipiters and Buzzards, but I recorded it only five times for my Kestrels, always by a female, twice in February and once each in April, July and September. Each time it was performed at low level and the female was followed by a male, who was either 'shivering' or calling. I have seen this display too infrequently to guess its significance but twice it occurred between birds which later proved to be paired, which suggests that it is a courtship display.

Three times (twice in November and once in January) I recorded the leapfrogging along a line of perches which was described by P.M. Walsh in Cramp and Simmons (1979). I saw this too rarely to gauge its purpose, but once as part of a prolonged display in January by an immature male courting a widow.

Females also occasionally perform 'parachuting' flights, planing around or down on set wings, usually with talons dangling; I have seen this once from a male, as well. This display is common among Buzzards. For Kestrels I have seen it only during extended territorial arguments – once from a female above two males which were fighting furiously on a thorn hedge. Perhaps these are infrequent because they all appear to be largely female displays.

Adult male Kestrel in rocking flight display (see page 68), *high and fast, with flight surfaces tightly slimmed.*

Two male Kestrels fighting. The lower bird eventually wriggled free and departed hastily, although apparently unharmed (see page 68).

Perched displays

Territorial disputes among Kestrels often end with the protagonists sitting alert on exposed perches, watching. Such prominent perching also occurs independently of other displays and seems to be an important method of marking territories. Most individuals have several favourite perches in their territories or hunting ranges, where they spend much time, particularly in winter. Sometimes they hunt from them but often they just sit. The fact that the perches are exposed and that Kestrels sometimes sit on them in very poor weather suggests that they are more than loafing sites. They are not necessarily at the edge of territories but, if this behaviour is territorial defence or marking, which I suppose it to be, a good field of view is probably as important as being highly visible to the perched bird. Such behaviour is much less frequent in summer, when it would be largely unnecessary because birds effectively advertise their presence by hover-hunting. Courtship and territorial behaviour in Kestrels also involve other perched displays, such as bowing, mutual bill- and toe-nibbling and food-begging. These are usually difficult to observe accurately in the field but have been detailed for captive birds by J.K. Kirkwood (in Cramp and Simmons 1979).

Territorial boundaries

Kestrels' territories tend to be marked by distinct boundaries. Such boundaries are not inviolable in the sense that a pair's territory will always be delineated by the same features. In one year, for example, changes in nest sites by two neighbouring pairs in my Sussex area led to their territories shifting

71

from a roughly north-south axis to a roughly east-west one, crossing previous boundaries. At any one time, however, several factors indicated that territory boundaries tended to be drawn along physical features of the landscape. One was the point also made by Village (1990), that a Kestrel can be pushed only so far along a line of posts or a road or similar features before it will fly around the observer and back into its territory at places such as a bend, a ditch junction, a single prominent bush or even a break in an otherwise continuous hedge line. Another was the frequency with which territorial arguments broke up over marked features such as hedge lines, roads and streams, or sometimes prominent isolated trees, each Kestrel diving away back into its own territory. A third indication was seeing Kestrels apparently patrol such a line in response to a territorial argument elsewhere. This was also noted by Pettifor (1983), and in Wales I notice this behaviour quite often between raptor species. I do not know if territorial boundaries would be so obvious in areas less well supplied than my Sussex site with linear features such as hedges and ditches, but Pettifor certainly also noted it in Cambridgeshire. In Wales, Kestrel pairs are too thinly spread for territory to be obvious, but Buzzards tend to align their territories similarly on physical features of the landscape.

Reactions to corvids and other raptors

Kestrels also have to share their hunting ranges and territories with both corvids and other raptors. Another form of territorial dispute comprises interactions with these species. These interactions may involve direct confrontations, such as mobbing, or more indirect reactions, such as one bird shifting in response to movements by the other.

In the breeding season, my Sussex Kestrels shared their range with one or two pairs of Sparrowhawks; Little Owls, Tawny Owls and Barn Owls also bred, and Hen Harriers, Merlins and Short-eared Owls wintered regularly in small numbers. By contrast, Kestrels share my Welsh study area with six other breeding species of diurnal raptor, of which Buzzards and Sparrowhawks are both numerous, and I estimate the overall density of breeding diurnal raptors to be 49–50 pairs per 100 km^2; Tawny Owls are also numerous and Barn Owls are present. Interactions occurred between Kestrels and all the diurnal raptors and are summarized in Table 5.2. Although infrequent in Sussex, they were always of interest. Some surprising species also incurred the Kestrels' odium and I have records of males mobbing Pheasants and Great Black-backed Gulls near nests. In Wales such interactions formed a striking proportion of my sight records. Kestrels also reacted to corvids, which were abundant in both areas, but I have not tabulated these records, which were incomplete.

Corvids, particularly Magpies, quite often mob young Kestrels in the autumn but I think that adults are mobbed far less and that mobbing by corvids is probably rather infrequent at other times; such mobbing may often be attempted piracy, and adult Kestrels are perfectly able to deal with Magpies. In Wales, I have noticed that hunting Kestrels often evade the near presence of, or mobbing by, Carrion Crows or Ravens by flying rapidly out over the valley and then circling back behind them; such interactions have nuisance value but are probably not more significant.

Competition for nest sites may be. For example, although they frequently use the old nests of Ravens, I do not often find cliff-nesting Kestrels very close to active Ravens' nests in Wales. In Sussex, Kestrels certainly competed with Jackdaws for nest sites in hollow trees, for I several times watched Kestrels ejecting them (and once ejecting Stock Doves). One of a pair of Jackdaws driven out of a possible nest site by a full-blooded stoop from a female Kestrel was unwise enough to return while she was still there; it was violently assaulted, the birds falling out of the tree in a whirling tangle before the Jackdaw fled, shedding feathers. I also once found a Kestrel's nest scrape, in use (there were fresh pellets in it), only 45 cm above an incubating Jackdaw in a big elm stump. The female Kestrel died before laying, so I could make no further observations, but Roy Leverton once recorded a nest in which both a Kestrel and a Jackdaw had laid. As potential predators, it is Magpies that Kestrels appear most consistently and frequently to drive away from nests or their vicinity, especially those with small young. Although the BTO nest record cards give little information on the species responsible for preying on Kestrels' nests in Britain, Hasenclever *et al.* (1989) found Magpies to be the most important in Westphalia.

In Sussex, Kestrels occasionally displayed at Sparrowhawks but the most frequent interactions with other raptors were with harriers. Harriers often hunted over the preferred hunting sites of Kestrels, being particularly drawn to clover fields, for example. Kestrels sometimes mobbed the harriers severely, but, again, I doubt if such interactions represented serious competition. They did, however, produce some entertaining brawls. I once watched a male Kestrel soar up over its territory and attack a Hen Harrier,

Table 5.2 *The number of interactions between Kestrels and other diurnal raptor species noted in Sussex and Wales by season.*

	SUSSEX 1979–1981				WALES 1987–1990			
	Nov–Jan	Feb–Apr	May–July	Aug–Oct	Nov–Jan	Feb–Apr	May–July	Aug–Oct
Red Kite					1			1
Marsh Harrier			2					
Hen Harrier	4	3			1			
Goshawk								1
Sparrowhawk		1		3	1	1		5
Buzzard				1	7	11	7	21
Merlin				1				1
Peregrine					1		2	3
Total	4	4	0	7	11	12	9	31
Total Kestrel sight records	640	621	408	629	50	63	70	135
Interactions as a percentage of Kestrel sight records	0.6	0.6	0	1.1	22	19	13	23

passing high above, in a series of stoops and powered dives which steadily forced the harrier down to hedge-top height before it passed out of the Kestrel's territory. Such incidents can be seen anywhere where Kestrels occur with other raptors, and the ultimate may be John Reaney's record of one setting about a Griffon Vulture in Spain.

In Wales, 20 per cent of my sight records of Kestrels included interactions with other raptors, largely Buzzards. Reactions with Buzzards occurred uniformly through the year (Table 5.2), and 37 per cent of instances when Kestrels and Buzzards were both present in the same general area (which does not necessarily mean very close together) resulted in some reaction by the Kestrel to the Buzzard. The hunting behaviour of Buzzards in my Welsh area is remarkably similar to that of Kestrels., primarily hover-hunting in summer and still-hunting in winter; both species mainly hunt rough grass, young forestry and scrubby habitats. Buzzards also take many earthworms on improved grass fields in winter, which I have not recorded Kestrels doing in Breconshire, unlike in Sussex, although they take many insects from well-grazed swards. The overlap in hunting, however, is particularly marked in the breeding season when both species concentrate largely on small mammals, mainly voles and shrews. Buzzards seem rarely to take rabbits in the area (although rabbits are increasing rapidly, so that may change), but they prey frequently on fledgling Jackdaws and other corvids. They also tend to hover-hunt lower than Kestrels, which may well be significant as, if both species work around the same spot, the Buzzard will be below – classic territorial defence among Kestrels!

In these circumstances, Kestrels either shift out of the disputed area altogether, often mobbing the Buzzard *en route*, or keep a wide spacing between them, which usually results in the Kestrel being rolled along the ridge away from its preferred spot. Watching from a good overlook, it is often possible to see the two species alternating at the same site, the Kestrel returning if the Buzzard moves away and so on, behaviour not dissimilar to

Kestrels can be very aggressive to other raptors, perhaps particularly when breeding; size is no object!

that shown by neighbouring Kestrels. The frequency with which I see Buzzards move into areas in which Kestrels are already hunting, however, has led me to believe that they may be particularly attracted to hunt such sites. Effectively it is a form of piracy. I have little doubt that this is genuine competition in which the Buzzard is dominant and that it leads to a reduction in the number of Kestrels that the area will support. High and rising stocking rates reduce the amount of good vole habitat available, and competition from the dominant Buzzard then reduces further the area the Kestrels can freely use. Dare (1986) also suggested that Buzzards compete with Kestrels, to the latter's disadvantage, in north Wales, and that this contributed to the low density of Kestrels he found in Snowdonia.

Kestrels are also preyed upon by other raptors. Newton (1979) cited 113 cases of Kestrels being taken by Goshawks, two by Sparrowhawks and two by Peregrines; Ratcliffe (1980) listed eight records of their being taken by Peregrines and indicated that such records were more numerous; and Glue (1971) listed one each of Kestrels being taken by Hen Harriers and Buzzards. I have four records of Peregrines attacking Kestrels but none ended in a kill. I also once watched a brood of Kestrels retire to cover among some rocks when a Peregrine passed through their hunting area, emerging when it left. Mikkola (1983) lists 214 records of Kestrels taken by owls in Europe, but 91 per cent relate to Eagle Owls; Tawny Owl was the second most important predator, accounting for 7 per cent of the total.

I have, as yet, little direct personal evidence that such predation has serious implications for Kestrel numbers in my Welsh area, but I suspect that the widespread presence of Goshawks in many forest areas there may account for the paucity of Kestrels actually nesting in such sites, although they hunt in them. Jon Westlake has also remarked that forestry restocks are now used less than they were before Goshawks spread into the area, and I agree. In addition, in a study of Goshawk prey in four Welsh sites in one breeding season, two male Kestrels and one female were recorded (I. Williams, pers. comm.); with the low Kestrel densities, common in Wales that probably wrecked three breeding attempts. Kestrels also avoid nesting too close to Peregrines (Ratcliffe 1980), and Riddle (1987) noted that they lost a number of cliff sites in Ayrshire with the recovery in Peregrine numbers there in the 1970s and 1980s. I have noted this twice in my Welsh area, but its impact there is marginal because alternative sites in crows' nests are abundant.

I have also observed a curious piece of behaviour by hunting Kestrels in Wales, which may arise from the increased danger from predators. They can often be seen craning their necks when hover-hunting, to peer behind them. This is something I never noted among my Sussex birds, although I may have seen it and thought nothing of it. Perhaps the significantly shorter hovering times I have noted in Wales derive from the same cause – movement allowing the birds to check. Doubtless a hover-hunting Kestrel, concentrating on the ground below, is potentially very vulnerable.

6

BREEDING

FOR all bird species, breeding is the most important aspect of their life. There is much more to it than simply laying eggs and rearing young. For the Kestrel the whole process begins early in the year and, because of the various stages involved, is not completed until the end of the summer.

Early stages and pair-bond

Breeding activity in Sussex usually started from mid February, when males or pairs spent increasing amounts of time around nesting areas and mutual display started. In his upland Scottish area, Village (1990) found that migrant breeders started to return from mid February, as I have also noted in Breconshire. In Denmark, too, spring migrants start to return at that time (Nielsen 1983), but further north and east they are later, at the beginning of April in southern Finland for example (Korpimäki 1986) and late April/early May in Siberia (Dementiev and Gladkov 1951).

In Sussex, pairs sometimes formed before February. For example in two winters males were lost but their females stayed. In both cases, I saw new males, both immature, performing courtship displays with these females in early January and pairs apparently formed successfully. Both males, however, were eventually rejected in favour of adults. Pairs may also form with very little overt display. Thus, I lost a female on one territory on 21 January 1981 and her mate certainly had a new mate by 22 February, although I had seen no indication of courtship. The weather, however, was vile, which probably suppressed flying activity.

Pairs may remain together for more than one year, break up for winter and re-form in the following spring, or break up and choose different mates in the next spring. In Britain, lowland pairs are more likely to remain together in winter and upland pairs to separate, as many migrate, but Village (1990) found that fidelity to mate was very similar in both circumstances, so migratory behaviour per se has rather little influence. The most usual reason for a change of mate is widowhood, but divorce also occurs. Village found that such changes of mate were more likely after an unsuccessful breeding attempt. Kestrels are normally monogamous, but two records are known of females with two males and cases of males breeding with two females occur sparsely. The nest record cards of the BTO for 1950–87 include one definite and four probable cases of the latter in 3773 records; Village noted one case in his Scottish area and I had one in Sussex. Often difficult to prove without marked birds, it may be under-recorded, but there is no evidence that such polygamy is anything other than a regular but very uncommon phenomenon.

76

Some typical nest sites. Cliff ledges and abandoned stick nests are classic Kestrel sites but bale-ricks are more recent. Although commonly used, they are risky (see page 94).

Nevertheless, I once watched a bigamous pairing develop in Sussex and it was the second female which apparently took the initiative. I first recorded display involving her (recognizable because of a damaged wingtip) at a nest site with an established pair by my house on 2 April; she was doing a vigorous rocking display over the site while the resident adult male was circling under her, tail-fanning in a typical territorial defence and pushing her away. For the next fortnight I regularly noted displays, some very complex, over and around this site and an alternative one used by this pair about 700 m away, sometimes involving the pair, sometimes the male and the second female and sometimes all three birds together. They went through virtually the whole repertoire of flight displays, and the intruding female added some of her own – particularly dives and upward swoops and an extraordinary 'spiral staircase' display (see page 68) which I have never otherwise witnessed. On at least two occasions I found the second female displaying on her own, calling and investigating possible nest sites at the alternative site area. I also particularly noted that both the established female and the male were trying to drive this bird out of their territory.

The intense level of display activity died down after a fortnight, but the second female remained on the pair's territory. I saw no further attempt by the male to get rid of her but I also saw no sign that he was paying her any attention, although he regularly fed and copulated with his established mate. Nevertheless, on 30 April I found all three birds together and it was clear that the male had accepted both females, although his original mate was still trying to drive the second female away. On 16 May I discovered the original female dead in her nest scrape, almost certainly poisoned, and the second female on four eggs. These hatched around 8 June, indicating that laying started on 5 May, when I knew that both females were still active. While perhaps an exceptional case because of the death of one female, the male was certainly supporting both for a period. Furthermore, there was an unmated immature male at the other end of the farm, displaying over a practicable nesting area in late April/early May, which the second female ignored. The whole episode may give a useful insight into what actually happens in such cases.

Nest-site selection is by both sexes. Females may start examining potential sites up to seven weeks before laying, and the scrape finally used may be formed a month before. Typically, females clamber and potter about in trees, peering into holes, hopping in and out of them, making scraping motions and fluttering along to check another possibility. I have noted similar behaviour in buildings and on cliff sites, but not, curiously, at stick nests in trees, although Village (1990) describes it. The male may simply sit and watch, following the female rather as male finches do when their mates are building, or sometimes I have seen them perform mild displays around the tree the female was inspecting and also attempt coition. Males also investigate sites in a similar way, apparently trying to attract the female to a suitable one, and may do so with a 'butterfly' (page 69). Females often, perhaps regularly, make scrapes in more than one site, which may be well separated. In the latter case the pair will divide its time between the two, the male feeding the female at both for example, and a final decision on which to use may not be made until very near laying. Such behaviour probably has a useful function in assessing the safety or suitability of sites, and Village particularly observed that females sat in their scrapes in wet weather, perhaps to keep them dry and to check their weatherliness.

Copulation may occur up to eight weeks before laying, and has been recorded as early as January in the Netherlands (Masman *et al.* 1988). That it occurs so long before laying shows its important secondary function in maintaining the pair-bond. Towards laying it increases in frequency. Kirkwood (in Cramp and Simmons 1979) records various preliminary postures by captive birds, but, in the field, I have often noted no obvious preliminary, the male simply flying to the female and mounting her, wings held up above his back and fluttering, usually with much calling. Copulation usually occurs near the nest (but not necessarily at it), on branches or similar perches or on the ground, and males often display afterwards.

To accumulate the reserves necessary to form and incubate a clutch of eggs, the female progressively stops hunting (to conserve energy) and depends on the male for food. In six cases in Sussex, the date when females apparently stopped hunting, at least regularly, for themselves ranged from eighteen to 32 days (mean 25) before the first egg was laid. There was a quite strong negative relationship between the length of this period and clutch size, although it was not statistically significant because of the small sample. Such a relationship presumably reflected the ease with which the male could find food. If he is unable to feed his mate sufficiently at this stage, the breeding attempt will collapse. So long a period of dependence, however, is not necessarily typical. Migrant populations in northern Europe can scarcely afford it, and Korpimäki (1985b) noted that females in southern Finland were fed by their mates for only about a week before laying. As laying approaches, females spend most time at the nest. I found that males at this time, except when hunting, often spent long periods quietly sitting with their mates. Unless one watches a site all day it is difficult to tell how often males provision females at this stage (it will, in any case, vary with resources), but my records suggested that males typically brought food, mainly Short-tailed Voles, every two to three hours, indicating some four to six meals daily. The times I gathered for one pair in Sussex also suggested a rather regular routine, with particularly regular visits between 8 and 9 a.m., around noon and around 7 p.m. Generally speaking, the period around noon seems to be one of the most reliable times to spot males killing and taking food to females and nests.

When bringing food to nest sites, males either soar up with their catch and drift around rather aimlessly, clearly checking the area before diving in, or they approach low along a route which provides some concealment. Such behaviour clearly provides the nest with some protection. On approaching, males usually give a sharp 'kik' note and either the female comes out to collect the prey directly from the male or he leaves it in a larder. Prey is usually passed on a perch, but occasionally there is a food-pass in flight, the female flicking over on her side and taking it direct from the male's talons. The male will often display over the site after a delivery and some fine performances may be seen then.

This lengthy courtship is not strictly necessary for successful breeding, and there is much variation. Not only is the courtship generally shorter in northern populations with long migrations it also varies widely in temperate areas. Village (1990) remarked that he knew of no evidence that a long courtship was necessary for successful breeding and pairs bred successfully without. Its advantage seems to lie in conferring greater flexibility and a greater chance of breeding successfully in all conditions.

The age of breeding

Kestrels are sexually mature at one year but do not necessarily breed then Females are difficult to age in the field, and I have no information on the age of breeding females in my Sussex area. However, Village (1990) found that 41 per cent of pairings in his Scottish area and 21 per cent in his farmland areas involved young females (one-year-old birds); significantly fewer involved young males (21 and 9 per cent, respectively). In Sussex, 15 per cent of the pairings noted over seven years of recording breeding attempts in a 1500-ha area involved yearling males, but I never recorded successful breeding by any. In two cases young males paired with females which had bred the previous year were rejected for adults, in one case breeding was attempted but failed, in one the female vanished (perhaps poisoned), and in the last I was not sure whether what I recorded was attempted cuckoldry by an enterprising young male or whether that male, too, was rejected for an adult. In addition, one young male held territory but failed to attract a mate. In Wales in five years, I have found only one yearling male paired and attempting to breed, although sub-adult males sometimes hold territory.

Breeding is clearly more difficult for young males than for young females. Males have to provision the female and brood as well as themselves, which needs experience, and Village found that young males were more likely to breed in good vole years in Scotland than otherwise. In addition, males have to hold a nesting territory and a mate, and the strongly contrasting plumage of adult males is an important factor in this; young males, lacking it, are at a disadvantage, and it may partly be for this reason that adult females may reject young males. This, and the higher divorce rate among females, suggest that the female has the strongest role in selecting mates.

Nest sites

Kestrels do not build a nest, usually making a scrape in the material of the site selected. However, Walpole-Bond (1938) found they almost invariably removed the root lining from old nests of Magpies, and nest record cards include a crow nest in which the crow's clutch was smashed, the nest taken over by Kestrels and relined with sheep's wool to cover the mess. Dementiev and Gladkov (1951) also mention the addition of lining material by Kestrels.

Four basic types of nest site are used by Kestrels in Britain: ledges, old nests or holes in cliffs, holes in trees and abandoned stick nests of other species in trees, and ledges or holes in buildings. Nests on open cliff ledges are often sheltered by a tree or rock. Nestboxes are increasingly being

A pair of Kestrels prospecting an old weather-boarded barn. Barns, particularly stone barns, are an increasingly commonly-used nesting site.

provided in southern England, and these are often favoured sites which may be attracting Kestrels from natural sites. There are marked geographic variations in the distribution of site use (Figure 6.1, overleaf). Not surprisingly, cliff sites predominate in the uplands, but chalk cliffs and quarries seem to be rarely recorded, either because Kestrels infrequently use them or because they are particularly difficult to check. There is some evidence, however, that use of such sites may have declined (Shrubb 1970). Sites in rural buildings show a remarkable and increasing concentration in north-west England. Sites in urban areas are predominantly buildings and are not shown.

The predominance of nesting in tree holes in the English lowlands represents a marked historical change. The early literature stresses that old stick nests in trees were the main nest site there in the nineteenth and early twentieth centuries. The change continued through the period 1937–87, but it does not seem to have been due simply to such factors as Dutch elm disease increasing the number of hollow trees, having been firmly in place before the late 1960s. Rather, it seems to have arisen because farmland and hedgerow trees particularly are no longer regarded and managed as a useful economic resource, greatly increasing the number of ageing and decrepit trees present. The distribution of use of tree holes by Kestrels is also closely correlated with tillage in farmland. Thus, it seems likely that farmland trees, perhaps especially in hedges, are deleteriously affected by modern cultivation techniques; this applies particularly to Ash, which is shallow-rooted and the most frequent tree used by hole-nesting Kestrels (Shrubb 1993). The change is exemplified by records for Cambridgeshire, where Lack (1934) noted that virtually all Kestrels bred in old stick nests in trees because of a lack of old timber in farmland and Easy (1990) recorded no such sites among 125 pairs, nests being in tree holes, buildings and chalk pits.

There is no evidence that the loss of hollow hedgerow trees to hedge clearance and Dutch elm disease caused a serious loss of nest sites. Assuming so ignores the fact that the present scale of use of tree holes by Kestrels is a recent change and that old stick nests in trees are increasingly abundant with

81

Figure 6.1 *The most frequently recorded Kestrel nest sites in rural areas in Britain by county (by region in Scotland) (1937–87). Where two or more sites were equally important shadings are arbitrarily divided. Nest boxes are excluded.*

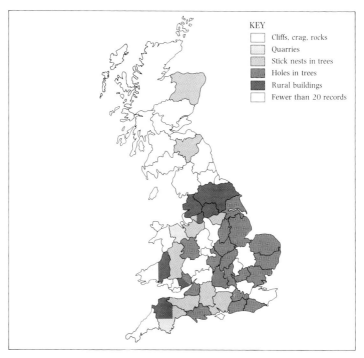

KEY

- Cliffs, crag, rocks
- Quarries
- Stick nests in trees
- Holes in trees
- Rural buildings
- Fewer than 20 records

Source: BTO nest record cards.

the vast increase in crows and Magpies (Marchant *et al.* 1990). The species of trees used by hole-nesting Kestrels may differ from those used by the common owl species, and Kestrels tend to nest in holes that are higher up the tree, not just in holes in branches but also in holes in the main stem. They also often use the open cavities formed by snapped-off tops of trees ('chimneys'), which are not used by Barn or Little Owls (Shrubb 1993).

The most frequent stick nests recorded are those of crows in conifers, especially Scots Pine. The frequency with which the latter are used in much of lowland England seems disproportionate to the number of pines present, suggesting a preference by Kestrels. Kestrels are selective of stick nests in other ways: they generally avoid low nests of crows and Magpies, and I found that they were more likely to use stick nests in trees that stood in company, in woods or shelterbelts etc., than in isolated trees. This may result from predation, which may influence choice of nest site among small raptors (Newton 1979). Predation is not only more frequent in stick nests in trees than in the other main Kestrel sites but, in the former, is also less frequent where trees are in clumps rather than isolated (Shrubb 1993).

Most of the stick nests used by Kestrels are abandoned nests of the previous year, but the falcons are capable of ejecting Magpies and crows from new nests, a behaviour once regular in Lancashire (Oakes 1953). It now seems rare (the nest record cards note only two cases in fifty years), but Kestrels more often take over newly built nests from which the corvids have been destroyed. In rural buildings Kestrels use mainly holes in or the tops of walls, sites which differ markedly from those selected by Barn Owls (see Shawyer 1987). Both species use bale ricks but Barn Owls use them far more often. In towns holes in masonry are the most frequent site used by Kestrels, but they are also fond of vents for heating or air conditioning!

Besides those noted in Figure 6.1 there are broader geographic variations in nest-site use in Europe. In Germany, nests in buildings are recorded three times more often than they are in Britain and old stick nests seem to be more frequent both in broadleaved trees and in the use of Magpies' rather than crow nests (Cramp and Simmons 1979; Hasenclever *et al.* 1989). In southern Finland nests recorded by Korpimäki (1985b) were in stick nests in trees, nest-boxes and buildings, and in Limousin, central France, buildings, stick nests in trees and tree holes, in that order, were the sites used (Noré 1979). Such differences perhaps do no more than reflect the resources available to Kestrels, but this may well be affected by nest-site use among other predatory birds.

Young Kestrel exercising wings at the nest, a prelude to flying.

Colonies and semi-colonies have been seen in the same range of sites. In stick nests in trees, these are not necessarily of colonial species such as Rooks; an accumulation of old nests in a wood may serve, for example.

Kestrels regularly use the same site in successive years and known instances involved 8 per cent of the total nest record cards for 1937–87, although Village's work showed that it was likely to be different individuals using the site. Some, possibly many, Kestrel sites have a longer history of use. Among long-term examples I have found are: Chichester Cathedral, used regularly during the 1960s and 1970s and also recorded as a regular site by Borrer (1891); two cliff sites in Ayrshire, used from 1970 to 1978, which were also recorded in 1898 and 1926 respectively (Riddle 1979); and, in the nest record cards, a hollow-tree site at Bodicote, Oxfordshire, said to have been used regularly from the late 1920s until it was felled in 1969.

Some esoteric sites are used by Kestrels, mainly in urban areas, such as mobile cranes, buildings under construction and windowboxes. The nest record cards include a Raven's nest in Orkney built of fence wire and baler twine. Mead and Pepler (1975) recorded five instances of Kestrels nesting in Sand Martin colonies, and Dementiev and Gladkov (1951) record them nesting in Roller burrows. Kestrels nest on the ground in Orkney, usually in tall dense heather, often in cracks in the ground (Balfour 1955). Such ground nesting is rare in mainland Britain, presumably because of predators. Dementiev and Gladkov also recorded it in the Soviet Union.

Kestrels will share a hollow tree or a building with other species, and the nest cards note it with Barn Owl (thirteen times), Jackdaw (seven), Stock Dove (six), Shelduck (four), Little Owl (three), sparrows and Tawny Owl (two each) and once with Black Redstart. Usually the sites are separate, but the Black Redstart and at least one Barn Owl used the Kestrel's entrance.

Nest dispersion

Kestrels' nests are rarely evenly dispersed through their environment as those of Sparrowhawks are (see Newton 1986), because they are dependent on features which are not regularly dispersed. Broadly, nest dispersion follows three patterns. In habitats like lowland farmland, nests are well, if irregularly, spaced because of territorial behaviour. In habitats such as open hill grazings or extensive forestry plantations, where potential sites may occur in patches in a uniform hunting habitat, nests may be more clumped, but this is not always so; in upland Wales Kestrels' nests tend to be widely and rather evenly spread. Colonial or semi-colonial nesting occurs where food is plentiful and usable nest sites limited to a few places (where they may be abundant). Such colonial breeding has been recorded in Germany, Morocco, Jordan, the Ukraine and Japan. Interestingly, the literature suggests that such colonies often exploit abundant populations of large insects for food.

These are not separate and distinct categories. Rather, nest dispersion shows considerable variation according to local conditions of food or nest sites. Regular colonial nesting has not been recorded in Britain, where nests are usually separate. The nest cards include only 21 instances in fifty years of pairs nesting within 200 m of each other: two pairs ten times, three

Kestrels do not build a nest. These eggs are laid in a scrape hollowed in straw bales.

pairs seven times and four or five pairs twice each. Of these, 52 per cent were in forestry or moorland habitats and 33 per cent were urban or suburban.

Colonial or semi-colonial breeding may occur temporarily where food becomes superabundant in an area with a more normal distribution of nest sites. This does occur in Britain. During the great vole plagues in the Borders in 1891–93, Adair's 1891 records included a colony of six nests in one wood and Gladstone (1910) noted eighteen nests in the Devil's Beef Tub near Moffat, Dumfries. These concentrations dispersed as the vole plagues died out.

Timing of nesting

With most bird species, nesting is timed so that young are in the nest when food is most abundant. This does not appear to be strictly true for Kestrels, since small mammals are most abundant in autumn (as are large insects in Britain), not late June–July (Corbet and Southern 1977). Although this may be partly offset by the availability of young birds as food, it effectively means that young Kestrels first become independent when food is most readily obtained.

North of the tropics, Kestrels breed in the spring, coming into breeding condition with lengthening daylight (Newton 1979). Within that broad framework, however, there is much variation. The timing of nesting is examined here on the basis of the start of laying. Strictly, as the previous sections make clear, the breeding season has in many areas been in progress for some time at that point, but the date when laying starts provides a convenient point for comparison which is unequivocal and has been fairly widely recorded.

In the nominate race, laying takes place between March and early June. It generally starts earlier in the south: this may be because of a longer laying season rather than because the bulk of the population lays earlier. Both

Kestrel chicks are not the prettiest! Note the wing quills just showing, so 10–14 days old, and clearly healthy.

points are made clear by the timing of laying in Britain shown in Figure 6.2. This assesses the time of laying against three altitude bands, but is also effectively a geographic split as most land below 150 m in Britain is in the south-east and most over 300 m is in the north and west; Scotland is shown separately. Laying starts earlier on low ground in England and Wales, basically the warmer and drier south-east, and is later as one goes uphill north and west, both in terms of when laying starts and of median first-egg date (by which half of all clutches were started). This does not apply in Scotland, where, although laying may start later, the median is earlier than in England and Wales. Northern and upland populations in Britain are also more migratory and the figure suggests that the laying season may be more compressed there, particularly in the Scottish uplands. In England and Wales and in Scotland, the tendency for laying to be later on high ground in the former and earlier in the latter has been consistent over time.

Several studies in Britain and Europe have shown that weather affects laying date (e.g., Cavé 1968; Riddle 1987; Village 1990). Laying is later in cold wet springs because rainfall inhibits Kestrels' hunting and may also inhibit vole activity (Cavé 1968); thus, food is more difficult to obtain. In the Netherlands, laying is also earlier following mild winters because these affect the condition of the female (Cavé 1968). In Britain, where the winters are milder, such effects seem to be less marked, perhaps because Kestrels show a greater tendency to move away from northern and upland

Figure 6.2 *The timing of laying by Kestrels in England and Wales and in Scotland according to altitude.*

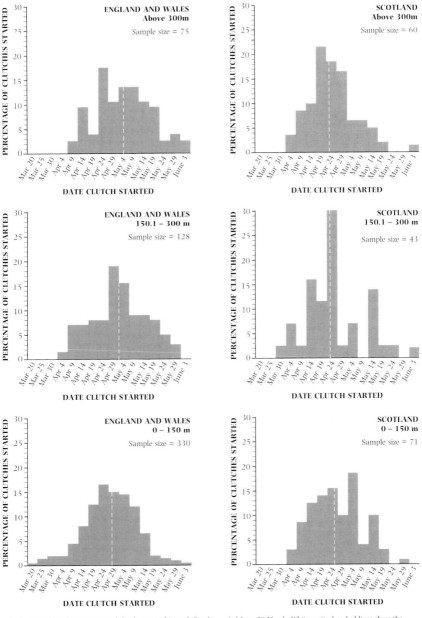

Histograms show the percentage of clutches started in each five-day period from 20 March. White vertical pecked lines show the median first-egg dates. Data from BTO nest record cards during 1950–87. Urban nests are excluded.

Interfering with Kestrels' nests is risky for Magpies (see page 93).

areas where winter is most severe and snow cover most likely. Village also found that females more often left his upland Scottish area than did males. Nevertheless the BTO record cards show that laying following the severe winters of 1962/3, 1978/9 and 1981/2 was later than average, as it was in 1975, following a wet spring, and in 1977, after a similar one. Weather, especially rainfall, tends to show marked local and annual variations. So, although a wet spring may delay breeding, such effects may be rather unimportant in the long term unless part of a permanent trend.

The most powerful immediate influence on the time of laying is food supply. This has been demonstrated experimentally in the Netherlands by Meijer *et al.* (1988), who found that the time females laid could be manipulated by providing extra food. Providing this for pairs early in the season advanced laying by an average of ten days and supplying food late in the season did so by six days. These effects, however, depended on natural food supply, and extra food did not influence laying date in good vole years.

Thus, nesting is undoubtedly earlier on uplands in Scotland than elsewhere in Britain because a much higher proportion of good vole habitat there provides a more reliable spring food supply. Much of the ground above 300 m in Britain is used as rough grazing, particularly for sheep. Records from such upland rough grazings in England and Wales and in Scotland showed not only that laying started earlier in Scotland but also that the median first-egg date was eleven days earlier (26 April opposed to

7 May), a highly significant difference. Although this analysis excluded records from young forestry, the figures do not, in fact, vary if the latter are included (Figure 6.2). The management of rough grazings is probably a crucial factor, and this is largely a matter of stocking rates, especially of sheep. These are some three times higher in England and Wales than in Scotland, which is presumably reducing the availability of good vole habitats. In these circumstances, a wider spectrum of prey and a better spring climate, giving more time for hunting in the south-east, may lead to earlier nesting in improved farmland than in upland rough grazings in England and Wales.

In some European studies, laying in urban habitats has been recorded as earlier than in rural areas. In Britain, the nest cards show that, in urban areas, laying is earlier in England and Wales (median first-egg date 2 May) than in Scotland (6 May); it is earlier than in upland areas in the former but later in the latter. The sample for Scotland is very small, however.

There is little information available about the timing of laying in the past in Britain, although habitat changes discussed in Chapter 3 suggest that it may have changed. In one case this is certainly so. Walpole-Bond (1938) records that, for extreme West Sussex, where habitat changes have been important, pairs usually had full clutches by mid April, indicating that early in this century laying started in the first week of April; during my studies there the earliest date I had for laying was 16 April and the median first-egg date 6 May, suggesting a significant change.

Eggs are normally laid at two-day intervals but longer intervals may occur, particularly later in the clutch. The nest cards include several instances of a final egg being laid after an interval of up to seven days. Such instances, however, are rare.

Clutch and brood size

Kestrels lay between one and seven eggs in a clutch, but, in Britain, 70 per cent of clutches are of four or five eggs and five is the most frequent number (Table 6.1). Clutches of one or two eggs are perhaps open to the suspicion that they have suffered some predation, which may be difficult to detect.

Every breeding study of Kestrels has found that clutch size decreases with time. This is demonstrated by the BTO nest cards (Figure 6.3). Dutch work has shown that mean clutch size declines by about one egg for every 23 days' delay in laying, and the British results reveal a comparable pattern. In the Netherlands, too, it was found that age did not influence clutch size,

Table 6.1 *The number of clutches of different sizes laid by Kestrels in Britain during 1950–87. The mean for Scotland was significantly larger.*

| | CLUTCH SIZE (NUMBER OF EGGS) | | | | | | | | |
	1	2	3	4	5	6	7	Mean	SD
Number of clutches in England and Wales	7	22	56	188	306	102	8	4.6	1.04
Number of clutches in Scotland	1	1	10	19	53	40	3	5	1.4
Source: BTO nest record cards. SD – Standard deviation									

Figure 6.3 *Clutch size of British Kestrels in relation to laying date.*

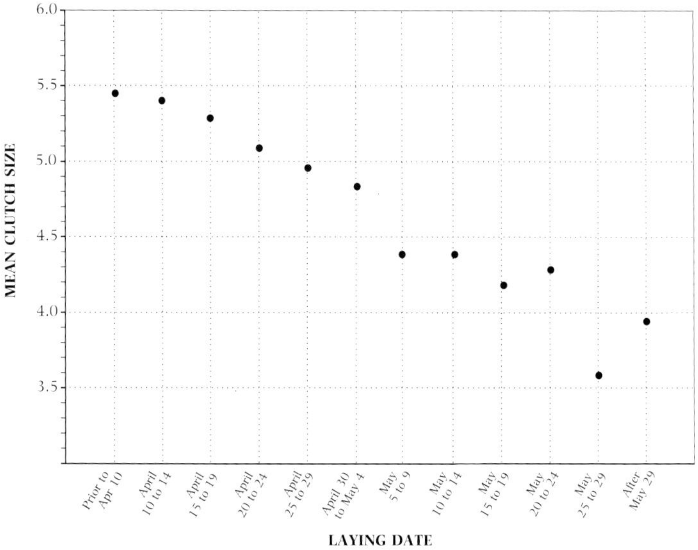

Mean clutch size is shown for each five-day period from 20 March, except that records up to 9 April and from 30 May are pooled because of small sample sizes. Source: BTO nest record cards.

young and old birds laying clutches of similar size for the date. Similarly, individual birds laid large or small clutches in successive years according to whether it was an early or late year. Experimental work with captive Kestrels showed further that, although food supply strongly affected laying date, it did not directly influence clutch size; this was controlled by date, irrespective of the amount of food offered (Meijer *et al.* 1988).

Clutch size is significantly larger in Scotland than in England and Wales because of the earlier laying dates (Figure 6.2). This was particularly marked in rough grazing and moorland habitats, where median laying dates were eleven days earlier in Scotland. During the 1970s and 1980s, when stocking rates, especially of sheep, were rising quickly in England and Wales, average clutch size in these habitats there was 4.48, compared with 5.02 in Scotland. Clutches in England and Wales are also generally smaller than in other parts of Europe. Recent studies have shown mean clutch sizes of 5.22 in the Netherlands (Meijer *et al.* 1988), 5.14 in Westphalia (Hasenclever *et al.* 1989), and 5.13 in Switzerland (Cramp and Simmons 1979). There is also much annual fluctuation in clutch sizes. In the Netherlands, for example, mean clutch sizes ranged annually from 4.03 to 5.62 in the 1960s and 4.59 to 5.53 in the late 1970s and early 1980s, and the BTO nest record cards show similar variations in Britain during 1950–87. In neither country did clutch size show any consistent trend over time.

Kestrels' eggs are lovely things; Walpole-Bond, a life long egg-collector, described them as of 'haunting' beauty at times. The ground colour may be white, with bold rich brownish-red streaks and blotches. Often, however,

Two clutches of Kestrels's eggs, to show something of the range of colour and shape which commonly arises.

the ground itself is pigmented with a paler reddish and the egg then appears red with darker markings, and some are zoned, with the red markings usually heaviest at the broad end. As well as varying among females, such colour differences appear in the same clutch and often may be pronounced, although their extent is very variable. Most clutches I have seen, however, showed some gradation. Eggs showing less red in a clutch are, I think, laid later in the sequence. There are often also subtle variations in size and shape, some eggs being noticeably more pyriform and some oval. Again these variations occur within as well as between clutches.

In Britain, the nest record cards for 1950–87 reveal that 67 per cent of Kestrels' nests hatched at least one young and that 73 per cent of all eggs laid hatched. Table 6.2 shows those nests followed right through the nesting cycle and compares the success of clutches of different sizes. In this sample, although fewer eggs in small clutches hatched, their hatching success did not vary with time of laying (although early clutches of this size were infrequent). That small clutches always had comparatively poor hatching success may support the idea that they were sometimes the result of partial predation, the predator returning to finish the job! Time of laying did, however, influence hatching success in clutches of four, five or six (see note to Table 6.2). Nevertheless, once hatched there was no significant difference in fledging success, nor was there between large and small clutches whenever laid. Clearly, early laying not only results in more eggs but also in more successful ones. This results mainly from the number of infertile eggs laid, infertility being the commonest cause of failure before hatching, followed by desertion (Table 6.3). This again is presumably a function of food supply. Laying is delayed when this is poor and the male finds increasing difficulty in feeding enough to the female for her to form and lay a clutch; as this difficulty increases, the likelihood of laying also declines. Such conditions will continue to affect the male's ability to provision his mate during incubation and, if food runs short then, she will desert. I found no relationship, however, between the time of laying and the incidence of nest desertion in the nest record cards, probably because nests are deserted for other reasons, especially human interference, which obscures the pattern. Once through this period, however, pairs usually succeed in rearing some young, and 91 per cent of the nests which hatched (in Table 6.2) fledged at least one. This perhaps reflects the availability of young passerine birds to augment food supply.

Whilst Table 6.2 fairly compares the performance of differently sized clutches, it may not be strictly representative of the breeding success of British Kestrels overall. Nest record cards tend to overestimate nesting success, as nests which fail, being more difficult to find, are underrepresented, thereby inflating the apparent level of success (Newton 1974). Statistical techniques circumvent this problem, and applying them to the cards suggests that about 67 per cent of Kestrels' nests hatch at least one young rather than the 75 per cent in the sample in Table 6.2. Once eggs hatch, a level of about 90 per cent of nests producing at least one young seems to be general.

Table 6.2 *The hatching and fledging success of Kestrel clutches of different sizes in Britain during 1950–87.*

| | Clutch size | | | | | | | | |
	1–2	3	4	5	6	7	CS	BH	BF
Number of nests	23	44	100	69	66	6			
Eggs laid	38	132	400	845	396	42	4.54		
Chicks hatched	10	69	262	587	272	18		2.98 (3.99)	
Chicks fledged	10	52	203	463	232	17			2.39 (3.88)
Percentage of eggs laid producing fledglings	26	39	51	55	59	40			

The sample comprises only clutches whose fortunes were followed right through the breding season, providing accurate information at each stage.
A total of 103 nests failed to hatch at least one chick and thirty nests which hatched failed to fledge any young.
CS – mean clutch size. BH – mean brood size at hatching. BF – mean brood size at fledging.
Figures in brackets are the means for successful nests observed.
Proportionately fewer eggs in small clutches (1, 2 or 3 eggs) hatched – $X2/1 = 30.43$, $P<0.01$.
More eggs hatched in clutches of 4–6 if laying started before 1 May – $X2/1 = 6.99$, $P<0.01$.
Source: BTO nest record cards.

As with clutch size, the nest record cards for Kestrels show little consistent trend over time in hatching and fledging success, despite annual variations. Nor do they show that the species' breeding performance has been greatly affected by pesticide use in Britain, which profoundly affected the breeding of Peregrines and Sparrowhawks, despite the impact that organochlorines appeared to have in terms of mortality in eastern England (page 35).

Causes of nest loss

The principal causes of nest loss are summarized in Table 6.3. This expresses losses in terms of eggs laid. Many otherwise successful nests lose part of the clutch or brood, so partial and total losses are shown separately. Besides the losses tabulated, these nests also lost 1112 eggs (10.6 per cent) to unknown causes, 320 in nests which were totally lost (70 per cent at the egg stage) and 792 as partial losses in otherwise successful nests (77 per cent at the chick stage). Clutches robbed or predated may be replaced.

Most of the unexplained partial losses were probably due to chicks dying of starvation. If so, this was the most important cause of loss. About a third of all nests which produced fledged young lost at least one chick in the process. There is much annual variation, which probably reflects mainly weather conditions and food supply. Wet weather in June, by curbing the adults' ability to hunt, can cause heavy losses if it coincides with the early nestling period, as the female cannot leave the chicks to hunt. Most such losses occur in the first ten days or so after hatching, and broods which survive intact to twenty days have a very high probability of all fledging.

The second most important cause was infertile eggs. The proportion laid in Britain has apparently increased over time, perhaps as Kestrels have spread back into habitats such as tilled farmland in eastern England since the early 1960s; this increased infertility is largely offset by a decline in the proportion of young hatching but failing to fledge. Nest desertion was highest in tilled areas in southern and eastern England: males perhaps had greater difficulty in supporting laying and incubating females in such habitats. Thus, losses in these habitats involved more total nest losses, but partial losses were fewer.

Kestrels suffer comparatively little from nest predators other than Man, but, besides avian predators, they may lose nests on sites such as bluffs to

Table 6.3 *The main causes of nest loss in British Kestrels during 1950–87. Losses are presented in terms of eggs laid (see text).*

	Infertile	Deserted	Robbed	Predated by Man	Destroyed	Died
Total nest losses	83	411	330	177	146	98
Percentage of eggs laid	0.8	3.8	3.1	1.6	1.4	0.9
Partial losses	725	0	65	8	0	179
Percentage of eggs laid	6.7	0	0.6		0	1.7

Notes: partial losses are eggs or chicks lost in otherwise successful nests. Robbed means contents taken by Man.
Source: BTO nest record cards.

Weasels. Kestrels' reactions indicate that Magpies are probably the most important avian nest predator, as found in Germany, and I have seen Kestrels attack Magpies near their nests. Man, however, is by far the most important predator of Kestrels' eggs and young shown by nest record cards. Including nests that were inadvertently destroyed, humans caused 75 per cent of losses to predation, including robbery and destruction of nests, and the loss of 5 per cent of eggs laid. Nests may be robbed, destroyed deliberately (mainly by game-preserving interests) or destroyed inadvertently, particularly by farm work. Nests in agricultural buildings are vulnerable to the latter, especially if in bale stacks. This was the primary cause of nest losses in Sussex. Losses to Man involve mainly eggs, but 30 per cent involved chicks. These are often taken as pets or by quasi falconers. Mather (1986) noted that the film *Kes* triggered a drastic increase in the taking of young Kestrels for pets in the 1960s and 1970s in Yorkshire, and I doubt it was confined to that county.

Care of eggs and young

Although I am not aware that the point has ever been checked at night, incubation is virtually entirely by the female. Incubation starts before laying is completed, but its timing varies with clutch size and females start incubating later with large clutches (Beukeboom *et al.* 1988). Village (1990) suggested that nearly all females in fact started serious incubation

Female feeding young at nest. Here she is feeding them entrails.

Well-feathered youngsters 'bill-nibbling', behaviour which also occurs as a courtship display between adults (see page 71).

on the fourth day before laying finished, although Brown (1976) noted that incubation sometimes starts with the first egg. Virtually all food is supplied to the female by her mate, but I have two records of incubating females also finding food for themselves: one nest failed but the other was successful. The latter was an exceptional case, however, for we were spreading spoil from a winter ditching operation near the nest. Both birds of the pair discovered this and followed the work daily, taking earthworms and other invertebrates. Our tractor driver found them some embarrassment for they would sit alert almost on top of his digger bucket, waiting like Robins at a gardener's spade. He once described the female as almost standing on her head trying to get some titbit from under a clod too heavy for her to push over; so he gently obliged with his bucket. He knew the difference between male and female Kestrels well and noted that the female would pop up to feed at intervals throughout the day. I have little doubt that, during the three or four days we were doing this work, the male did no more than relieve the female so that she could go and feed; I actually saw it happen once.

Normally, however, the male brings prey to the female, who feeds nearby, often on a regular site which can become very obvious. My records suggested that the demand from incubating females was rather less than during later courtship and laying. The times I most frequently recorded males provisioning incubating females were early and mid morning and late afternoon, but I did no all-day watches so did not accurately record the number of visits daily. In the Netherlands, however, Tinbergen noted that four incubating females he studied consumed between five and thirteen prey items daily, with an average of 9.3. Such variations in the frequency of provisioning reflect the differing sizes of prey items brought, and other Dutch workers estimated the energy intake of incubating females at c. 309 kJ daily, about 17 per cent less than during laying (Village 1990).

I found that incubating females, when feeding, were usually off the nest for about twenty to thirty minutes, long enough to feed, preen, stretch, and defecate – which is never done at the nest, although pellets may be cast there. Although rarely far away, they may stay off for longer periods in the morning and I recorded times then of up to an hour and a quarter. The male often covers the eggs for at least some of the time the female is off, and he always remains in the area on guard.

Most female Kestrels in my experience are very tight sitters, but this may be coloured by the fact that most nests I have watched were around farms, where sitting females learn to ignore human comings and goings. Kestrels' tolerance of disturbance is widely recorded, and they will become quite blasé if work goes on around them regularly and daily, sitting and watching with keen interest. One female also learned to recognize my car and would then circle it, protesting, if I stopped anywhere near her nest; if I wanted to use a car as a hide to watch, I had to borrow my wife's!

The length of incubation varies. Brown (1976) and Cramp and Simmons (1979) note an average of 27–29 days per egg, but Village (1990) found that the period from the start of incubation to the hatching of the first egg varied from 26 to 34 days, with a mean of 31. I have little information on the subject but what I have supports Village. Because incubation normally starts before laying is complete, hatching is spread over a shorter period than laying. Brown suggested three to five days as the hatching period for clutches of four or five. Village noted that even clutches of six may hatch in two days but also that hatching of such clutches may extend over nearly a week, with the first three or four eggs hatching together. The BTO nest record cards, however, suggest that such extended hatching is rather infrequent. Nevertheless, even a two-day age difference will be evident in a brood's development right through to independence. Hatching itself is exhausting work, and some mortality is common at this point.

As during incubation, the male brings all food for the young in the early nestling stages, the female tearing it up and distributing it bill to bill, in small pieces at first but, as chicks grow, in larger chunks. At nests I have watched, the female apparently took care to see that all the young got some, peering around and reaching over to feed ones at the back. Chicks die of starvation because they cannot compete successfully for food, however, so food at these nests was presumably plentiful and such competition not important. Young hatch in a white down, with their eyes more or less closed and are closely brooded by the female for eight to ten days. The intensity of brooding, however, declines progressively, and the female first sits close by the young and then on a perch nearby where she can watch and guard.

The young grow quickly. They have voracious appetites from birth and gain weight rapidly. At birth they weigh 14–18 g, and that weight doubles in the first two days and may reach 100 g after seven. Maximum weight gain is between the second and third weeks, and most young attain 90 per cent of adult weight in about three weeks; weight declines a little in the last few days before fledging but then is still slightly greater than that of adults, providing some reserves for the first weeks out of the nest. Growth rates of parts of the body also vary, the feet and legs reaching nearly adult size before feathers emerge, for example (based on the account by Village 1990). Chicks' eyes are open at four days, the grey second down starts to grow at about a week and feathering starts at around two weeks, although wing quills appear earlier; young are usually fully feathered by 24–26 days and fledging averages 29 (Cramp and Simmons 1979; Village 1990; pers. obs.).

The male must increase sharply his killing rate once the young hatch, which, with voles at least, derives from more kills per strikes at prey, not more time hunting (Masman *et al.* 1988). This may not be so for Kestrels exploiting more varied food sources, and I noted a sharp increase in actual hunting activity in June in Sussex (Shrubb 1982). Nevertheless the Dutch authors also point out that the amount of time a Kestrel can spend in flight-hunting is limited by its own capacity for food (energy): their Kestrels rarely exceeded an average of 3.6 hours' flight-hunting daily, well within the limits set, and could not do more for very long even if prey were scarce.

The timing and frequency of feeds for the young by the female and prey delivery by the male often differ. The male leaves food in a larder and the female fetches it as she needs it. Figure 4.1 shows a marked bias towards hunting in the morning in the overall records for my Sussex area during summer, but my records of females feeding young were more evenly spread; these activities were probably adjusted to the most efficient pattern. As the young grow, the female increasingly leaves them and starts to hunt around the environs of the nest. Females are rarely far away and they are nearly always alert to potential trouble. Often they check the nest at intervals. How much hunting they do and when they start seem to be very variable. I have recorded females hunting as early as ten days after the young hatched, but, at other nests, the female appeared to do very little. The size of the brood, the availability of food and the efficiency of the male presumably govern this. It is probably also governed in part by the fact that the young do not start to feed themselves until about three weeks old, so the female is regularly drawn back to the nest by the need to feed them.

It is often difficult to be sure when a brood truly fledges, for their leaving the nest is a gradual process and starts with the young clambering about and perching in the vicinity. Over a period of a week or so they become visibly stronger on the wing, more adventurous and less attached to the nest site. I once watched a pair of adults apparently trying to draw their brood away from the nest site, but in the main the young appear to move away quite naturally. In the early stages the parents continue to bring food to the nest area, but, as the young spread away from the nest, the adults quite clearly have to look for them within the territory. Some broods may be very noisy at this stage but this is by no means invariable. Adults usually come in very high over the territory to locate young, and Michael Hollings records one male flying in with prey dangling very visibly below it in an extended foot. With one brood which I watched very closely, prey was still delivered regularly by the adults for seventeen days after the young left the nest and some was brought until 24 days; food was passed on the ground or, quite often, in the air, the young taking it direct from the adults' talons, and young were fed on a first-come-first-served basis. Other studies have suggested a period of dependency of a month (Cramp and Simmons 1979) and Masman *et al.* (1988) noted fourteen to 32 days.

Learning and play

Kestrels do not fledge with their skills ready made. These have to be learned by trial and error. I watched this process closely in a brood of four which spent their first month after fledging in the fields around my Sussex house. These birds first killed (beetles) for themselves ten days after first starting to leave the nest, and it was interesting to watch the exaggerated killing and mantling movements which accompanied these early forays. They quickly developed their skill and, at sixteen days, I was recording spells of two to three hours' continuous still-hunting, during which insects, nearly all ground beetles caught on stubbles or meadows, were often taken every two to four minutes. This supplied a substantial proportion of their daily needs and suggested clearly the route to independence. The birds used mainly power poles and cables as perches but also spread out along fence lines. Once these young Kestrels developed their skill, their behaviour at this activity was indistinguishable from that of adults.

I first noted these young hover-hunting eighteen to twenty days after fledging. Initially hovers were short, wobbly and low, but full-scale hover-hunting was observed by 27 days, when I also noted the first kill of a vertebrate item by one. Throughout the various stages of this development the age difference of the brood was evident; first two birds were doing it, then three, then all four. These youngsters subsequently roosted from time to time in one of our barns until they dispersed from the area, and their pellets showed quite clearly that insect prey remained their primary source of food. I believe this to be so for most young Kestrels in their first autumn, and it provides a bridge to learning to catch more difficult vertebrate prey. This learning process is very obvious. Young birds may attack ludicrous targets: I have seen them strike at Pheasants, and once the twitching ears of a hare, crouched in stubbles (I discovered that young Kestrels have a reverse gear when the hare sat up!), trying to catch things in standing cereals or vainly pursuing birds in flight, none of which experienced adults would bother with in normal circumstances. In Wales I have noted that young quickly learn to hawk flying insects. Their hunting technique is often also distinctive. For hover-hunting I found that young birds hovered lower than adults, a tendency confined to early autumn. More noticeable is that young birds sweep around the area they are hunting much more than adults do. Adults work a steady hover-shift-hover pattern, but a characteristic juvenile pattern is hover-shift-hover then sweep around the area, as though concentration is not fully developed. Perhaps such behaviour reduces the chances of piracy between siblings and of predation. A variant in Sussex was the 'Black Tern' technique: quartering a field at low level with short hovers, taking small items, covering the area and then swinging back downwind to start again. Youngsters also have to learn to strike successfully. An example of this was supplied by a juvenile which stooped magnificently at a Yellowhammer sitting in a bush, flicking on to its side and grabbing (and missing) as it hurtled past. An experienced adult would have attacked head-on and crashed straight into the target.

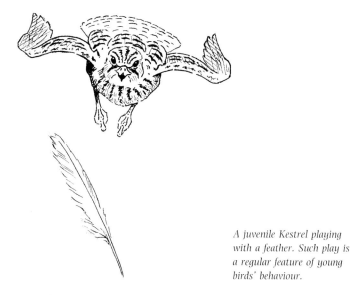

A juvenile Kestrel playing
with a feather. Such play is
a regular feature of young
birds' behaviour.

Juvenile Kestrels also play, a fairly common feature among young raptors. I have watched young Kestrels snatching such things as sheep-droppings from open hill, examining and discarding them, and catching feathers and going through the motions of 'killing' them. My brother, while hedgecutting, was accompanied by a juvenile for twenty minutes one afternoon, catching bits of broken stick as they spun out from under the cutting head; it was not always successful, and at least once performed an undignified crash-landing. Such play clearly has a valuable function. The most delightful record of this I have found, however, is from Gwent, where a pair of adults was watched for twenty minutes dropping sticks and balls of sheep's wool from a height of 15 m or so for their fledglings to catch (Gwent Bird Report 1990).

7

MOULT

FEATHERS perform vital functions in birds, not only of flight but also in regulating temperature and in weatherproofing (Thomson 1964) Kestrels, like all birds, spend much time preening and in general feather care. I have no personal record of their bathing, however, in the sense that Woodpigeons or Starlings do for example (taking a sponge and really getting down to it!). Brown and Amadon (1968) note that captive and falconers' birds of prey bathe (and drink) regularly, and Ratcliffe (1980) mentioned that Peregrines were fond of bathing (and dust-bathing), but Cade (1982) states that records of bathing by falcons generally are sparse. In their all-day watches of Kestrel activity in the Netherlands, Masman *et al.* (1988) make no mention of bathing.

Nevertheless, I have observed Kestrels rain-bathing. I was watching a male one July when it started raining: the bird flew straight to the top of a tree, spread his wings and tail, opened all his feathers and enjoyed a splendid shower. I saw this behaviour several times, and Hen Harriers in the area behaved similarly. I have also found Kestrels drying out after apparently bathing, spreading their wings and tail particularly to dry; although this occurred after rain whenever I saw it, there seemed no obvious reason for it unless the birds had deliberately become thoroughly soaked, something which Kestrels otherwise always avoid. I also have one record of a Kestrel drowning in a water trough, a cause of death which is surprisingly frequent in the ringing returns (page 120). I have never seen dust-bathing.

Despite regular care, feathers wear and have to be replaced. Kestrels moult all their feathers annually in a single moult.

Timing of moult

Moulting and regrowing feathers demands energy, largely from increased heat loss through declining insulation caused by dropping feathers. Other problems for Kestrels may arise from shedding flight and tail feathers, which may affect their hunting ability, although Cade (1982) remarked that falcons can lose quite a few tail or wing feathers without any obvious reduction in hunting performance. This certainly seems to be so with Kestrels, and it is possible to see some remarkably tatterdemalion adults hover-hunting effectively in late summer and early autumn. Whether they would be effective in such a state later in the year is another matter. Compared with other times of year living tends to be easier for Kestrels in late summer and early autumn: not only is the weather generally at its warmest and often most settled, but there is an abundance of insect prey and small-mammal populations are at their peak, so food is plentiful.

It is presumably for these reasons that moult is basically timed for early autumn, with the main period of feather-loss immediately after the young have fledged. Masman *et al.* (1988) noted that their Kestrels spent long periods inactive, to conserve as much energy as possible energy, at the peak of moult after fledging, a pattern also indicated by my hunting records in Sussex in July and early August (Shrubb 1982).

Moult starts earlier, however, and Village (1990) found that females typically began during incubation, after laying was finished. The mean date for 25 females in his Scottish upland area (where laying was earlier) was 11 May and for 35 on his farmland areas in eastern England was 26 May; males, having higher energy demands, started later – 31 May in Scotland and 5 June in eastern England. Both sexes may stop moulting if food becomes difficult to obtain during nesting. Village found arrested moult more frequent in males; it occurred in 20 per cent of the birds he checked altogether. The main period of moult lasts about 130 days (Cramp and Simmons 1979), although captive Kestrels in Holland did not finally complete moulting their body feathers until 180 days. Village found that males and females finished at about the same time, so moult is quicker in males.

The timing of moult may differ rather in migratory populations. For example, Dementiev and Gladkov (1951) note that Siberian populations show no sign of moult up to the end of May and that it usually starts in late June, finishing in the first half of September. As the few laying dates they give for northern and eastern Kestrels appear to be very similar to those for lowland England, this suggests a later and quicker moult in relation to the breeding season among these migrant populations. It is largely completed when migration starts. Further west they record moult from early June to mid September.

Juvenile moult and plumage

Juveniles undergo a partial moult of body feathers in their first autumn and winter but retain their flight and tail feathers until the following late-summer moult, which is complete and is timed as for adults. The extent and timing of the partial moult is very variable, but Village found that an increasing proportion of young birds he handled showed signs of moult as autumn progressed and all did during January to July. By no means all juveniles complete this body moult, however, and some juvenile body feathers may be retained until nearly two years old.

When juveniles first fledge, their wings often look distinctly rounded because the primaries have not finished growing. This appearance is lost quite quickly as these feathers complete their growth and probably suffer some wear. Cade (1982) noted that the flight feathers of most juvenile falcons are softer and more flexible than those of adults, suggesting that this might be an adaptation to compensate for greater clumsiness and inexperience in flight, reducing risk of possible damage in accidents. In many falcon species wing and tail length also tend to be greater in juveniles than in adults, but Kestrels show the opposite tendency, with juveniles having shorter wings and tail (Cramp and Simmons 1979).

Young Kestrels at about three-and-a-half to four weeks. One of these birds has distinctly greyish uppertail coverts and may, therefore, be a male.

Although juveniles also tend to be lighter, this suggests that there may be differences in wing-loading between adults and juveniles.

It is rarely possible to age or sex young Kestrels in the field unless by size, although in their first autumn they can usually be readily separated from adults by their bright, fresh and unworn plumage. Dijkstra *et al.* (1990), however, found that, in the Netherlands, nestlings, once feathered, could be reliably sexed on plumage, males having greyish uppertail-coverts with narrow pointed cross-bars. Cavé (1968), working in the same area, found a similar pattern. It is not clear how universal this is, as Village *et al.* (1980), in a similar study, noted that almost 20 per cent of those nestlings ringed in Britain which later proved to be males, had solid brown uppertail-coverts. Although these accounts seem contradictory, the tail pattern and colouring is a very variable feature in Kestrel populations and such variations are a marked racial characteristic of some (page 21). These discrepancies may therefore reflect genuine geographic differences.

Males do not assume fully adult plumage until their third year but acquire the grey tail, probably the most important feature of the distinctive male plumage, in their second autumn (Witherby *et al.* 1952).

Sequence of moult

In adults, moulting follows a fairly definite schedule. Uppertail-coverts and rump feathers usually start to moult before underparts or wing-coverts, and back and head feathers follow the latter; flight feathers start to moult before tail feathers. Primaries are now conventionally numbered from wingtip to body, and tail feathers from the centre outwards. Kestrels, like all falcons, start to moult their flight feathers at the centre and moult them both outwards (ascendantly) and inwards (descendently), beginning with the fourth primary; secondaries are moulted at the same time and in the same order. Tail feathers are moulted in the order one (central pair), six (outer pair), two, three, four and five (Cade 1982). Feathers on each side of the bird are dropped together, maintaining symmetry. Upperwing-coverts are moulted after primaries and secondaries (Cramp and Simmons 1979). The partial moult of juveniles in their first autumn seems to follow no clear-cut sequence.

A juvenile 'mantling' prey, a typically awkward and exaggerated effort. A male, note the grey tail, neat plumage and rounded primaries.

8

WINTER ROOSTS
AND ROOSTING

RATHER little attention has been paid to this subject where Kestrels are concerned. Yet, as a general principle, a lack of roosting sites may limit winter distribution just as a lack of nest sites limits breeding (Newton 1979). Although I am not aware that this has been recorded for Kestrels in the Palearctic region, the distribution of buildings and other sheltered roosts was found to govern the winter distribution of the American Kestrel in Ohio (G.S. Mills, quoted in Newton 1979).

Winter is a time of stress because poor weather, lower temperatures and short days both increase the individual's demand for food and reduce the time available to find it. For Kestrels, long periods of rough weather are as damaging as cold and may be more so than simply low temperatures, although snow cover poses severe handicaps. In these circumstances, a sheltered and relatively warm night roost would make a major contribution to conserving body heat, and therefore energy that must be replaced, in the long winter nights. In Sussex, all the roosts I found were well sheltered from the wind and rain. Most birds or pairs also had more than one regular roost on their territories. Quite probably, shifts from one roost to another resulted from changes in weather conditions (see also Yalden 1980). In addition, in one general roosting site, the actual perch was moved at frequent intervals, again probably in response to changes in the weather – as many of these were in open Dutch-type barns, perhaps particularly to changes in wind direction.

Roosting Kestrels are often remarkably indifferent to casual disturbance. One male that roosted above our herd of cows used to sit and watch me checking the cows at night during calving and would tolerate having a lamp shone at him, so I could easily check his comings and goings. Members of a pair may roost in the same building (although I do not think

Table 8.1 *Number of winter roosting sites in a Sussex study area.*

General sites used		Roosting perches	
Conventional barns and farm buildings	9	Doors and doorways	10
Dutch or open-fronted barns	6	Roof beams and rafters	7
Houses	3	Purlins and sheeting rails	6
Strawricks	2	Gutter and telephone fittings	4
Trees	2	Ledges in straw	2
Churches	1	Holes in straw	1
Summer houses	1	Window ledges	1

they often roost together), but I found that they frequently also roosted well apart, although meeting to sit together before roosting. One of my pairs often roosted in two buildings over 1.5 km apart. Possibly roosting separately and varying the site reduce the risk of predation, and it is interesting to watch Kestrels going to roost. Their approach is often roundabout and rather stealthy, with pauses on perches nearby to look around. Nevertheless, although Mikkola (1983) gave five instances of Kestrels being taken by Barn or Little Owls, Kestrels often roost in buildings used by these species in winter.

I rarely found Kestrels roosting in winter in actual nest sites, although they often used the same building. Presumably this is a matter of hygiene. In areas where large numbers of nestboxes have been erected, it would be interesting to know how frequently they are used as winter roosts and, if so, whether different boxes from those used for nests are selected.

Types of winter roost

During five winters in Sussex, I found a total of 24 different roost sites used by Kestrels in an area of *c.* 1500 ha (Table 8.1). Some of these sites were alternatives of the same pair or individual, and one of my pairs had four in regular use in the winter. The male was much more likely to shift site than the female, but she often shifted perches within her favourite site. Characteristically, these sites were in buildings and therefore well sheltered. Roosts in buildings are easier to find than those in trees (the other main site type available), so the latter may have been underestimated. However, I regularly checked lines and clumps of trees for signs of roosting, which are not difficult to spot, and also regularly checked birds into roosts, so I am confident that the table reflects accurately the roosting habits of my birds.

There are comparatively few observations on roosts. Witherby *et al.* (1952) noted sites in woodland or trees, holes in old buildings or clefts in cliffs. Papers on winter diet have mentioned roosts, such as a warm-air vent on a Manchester building (Yalden 1980), an old shed in Yorkshire (Ellis 1946), outbuildings at Menlough Castle, Ireland, (Fairley 1973) and a disused quarry in Pembroke (Davis 1975). In Wales I have also noted roosts in such sites as quarries and old buildings, and in Scotland Picozzi and Hewson (1970) found Kestrels roosting in quarries in forestry plantations in Eskdalemuir.

These last sites were a new feature of the habitat, being dug to supply road aggregates, but the Kestrels were quick to exploit them. Being semicircular, the roosts were well sheltered from most winds, and the Kestrels always perched under an overhanging mat of vegetation, giving shelter from rain. In northern France Thiollay (1963) noted roosting primarily in ruined houses and secondarily on cliffs, and winter visitors to India also roost mostly in ruins (Salim Ali and Ripley 1978). Brown, Urban and Newman (1982) state that Kestrels in Africa normally roost on cliffs and occasionally in trees. There seems to be a tendency for this species to use assorted buildings as winter roosts throughout its entire range, but,

again, these observations may be somewhat biased by the comparative ease of finding such roosts in buildings.

Some roosts, at least, are very probably traditional in the same way as nest sites are. One barn door on my farm was certainly used annually by Kestrels for twenty years until we pulled the barn down, after which the birds used its replacement. The frequency with which I found Kestrels using the same site in successive years elsewhere suggested that this was not an isolated case. Salim Ali and Ripley (1978) also noted that the roosting sites of winter visitors in India were often apparently traditional. This presumably rests on the fact that a good roosting site will be recognized by all Kestrels.

The actual perches used by Kestrels in Sussex also had several marked characteristics (Table 8.1). In conventional barns and buildings I was intrigued by the frequency of perches on doors or windows or by these openings – 70 per cent of the perches used. A favourite, where we kept the door of a barn pinned open, was to sit on top of the door, tucked against the wall under the eaves of the roof. If thatched, the eave might be 60 cm deep, giving splendid shelter. Perches on external walls, such as gutter brackets, invariably faced north or east, giving shelter from the prevailing south-west wind and rain; possibly cold was more tolerable than wet. In Dutch-type open barns the perches were usually right up in the peak of the roof, often at one end to take advantage of the cladding across the peak. Looking at perches, it was clear that Kestrels most often sat along them, like Nightjars, not across as is normal in daytime, with their bodies against the wall; doing so probably increased warmth and security. The perches described by Picozzi and Hewson in quarries in Eskdalemuir showed the same characteristics. The few tree roosts I have found were either in evergreens or sheltered by some sort of overhang.

Juveniles' roosts

I have rather few records of juveniles' roosting behaviour. One brood I watched closely during the post-fledging period certainly used the barn they were reared in but appeared not to do so every night. The evidence of droppings and pellets there also showed that they sometimes roosted together, but I do not know if this was always so. I also regularly found roosts which were used intermittently in the autumn but rarely in winter, and which I suspected were being utilized by young birds. Interestingly, these were always in fairly typical sites, which suggested that, if they were the sites of juveniles, these had an innate picture of a satisfactory roosting site. Young birds perhaps tend to look for a roost where they happen to be rather than use a regular site or sites. This would be an interesting subject to study in detail. So, too, would the sites used by migrants in transit, for which I can find no information.

ABOVE: *Juvenile Kestrels may miss surprisingly easy targets when first learning to hunt.* BELOW: *Sparrowhawks are fairly frequent victims of piratical behaviour by Kestrels; note that the bird was on the ground.*

Timing of roosting

In the Netherlands, Masman *et al.* (1988) found remarkably little seasonal variation in the time of roosting in their all-day watches. Kestrels ceased activity at about sunset and started about sunrise throughout the year. Such regular roosting behaviour is not universal.

Over 90 per cent of the prey taken in the Dutch study comprised Common Voles, which, active by day, had regular cycles of activity to which the Kestrels adjusted for hunting (page 56). Where more varied prey are taken, roosting may be much less regularly timed because, again, Kestrels adjust their activity to that of their prey. I have watched Kestrels hunting in Sussex much later than the roosting times indicated by Masman *et al.*, and such behaviour has also been reported by naturalists in Ireland at intervals since 1849 (Fairley 1973, for example). In Ireland and in lowland farmland in Britain, Wood Mice, much more nocturnal animals than voles, are major prey and much such late hunting is probably for this species. Village (1990) also suggested that his arable farmland Kestrels hunted birds at dusk to take them at a disadvantage. If successful the Kestrel will then feed, delaying roosting further. Nevertheless, so far as I can discover, such crepuscular behaviour seems to be rare outside Britain and Ireland, although Thiollay (1963) recorded it at Ushant (western France), again where voles were absent. It is also noted as occasional among resident African races, where Kestrels are otherwise recorded as returning to roost two to three hours before dark (Brown, Urban and Newman 1982). The roosting and activity rhythms of populations in southern Europe, which are much more dependent on large insects and reptiles, have hardly been studied; they may well differ again and be much more variable, as has been noted for Lesser Kestrel (Cramp and Simmons 1979).

A typical barn-door roost, tucked up under the eave for shelter and sitting along a narrow ledge (see page 107).

I have long had a suspicion that Kestrels may sometimes be active into the night or very early before dawn more often than the single incident (Roberts 1946) suggests. I quite often remarked in Sussex that changes in roosting sites coincided with moon phases which would have provided light at these times. This could be checked by radio tracking. Nocturnal activity has been surprisingly widely recorded among Western Palearctic falcons, being reported for Lesser Kestrel, Eleonora's Falcon, Sooty Falcon, Hobby and Peregrine besides Kestrel, while both Red-footed Falcons and Gyrfalcons habitually operate very late in the dusk (Cramp and Simmons 1979).

Kestrels do not use their roosting sites only during the night. Although they may sit out in it, marking territory, they tend to fly less in rain, as well as in snow and probably in fog and very high winds (Cavé 1968; pers. obs.). They often seek shelter in such conditions and can then be found in typical roosting sites, where they will sit out spells of bad weather, especially combinations of gales and rain, unless disturbed. Such weather also varies night roosting times, Kestrels retiring early and rising late in particularly unfavourable weather, as with many raptors.

Communal roosting

Many diurnal raptors roost communally during the winter and/or migration. The habit has been recorded for twenty out of 38 Western Palearctic species for which there is some information (data in Cramp and Simmons 1979); among falcons it is known for Lesser Kestrels, Red-footed Falcons, Merlins, Hobbies, Eleonora's Falcons and Sooty Falcons. It does not appear to be recorded for Kestrels in the Palearctic region nor in India and Pakistan, although I would have expected it sometimes where colonial breeding occurs or during vole plagues. Nevertheless, Palearctic migrants do roost communally in Africa, using cliffs and sometimes trees (Brown, Urban and Newman 1982); such roosts are smaller than those recorded for Lesser Kestrel, but little detail about them is otherwise noted. Palearctic migrants in Africa tend to be gregarious and insectivorous, attending grass fires and termite swarms for example, and Newton (1979) stated that gregarious behaviour among raptors is linked to exploiting such abundant but sporadic food sources.

9

MOVEMENTS AND MORTALITY

THE movements of Kestrels are of two sorts, dispersal and migration. Dispersal should not be confused with dispersion, which is concerned with spacing in a population. Dispersal is defined as a more or less random movement outward from the breeding locality after breeding (Thomson 1964). True migration denotes a regular movement between areas which are inhabited at different seasons, usually for breeding and wintering purposes. Distance itself is not a one of the criteria defining migration and some Kestrels which breed in mountainous regions will simply migrate downhill for the winter (Village recorded at least one bird in his upland Scottish area which did this). In practice, however, dispersal and such short-distance migrations may be quite difficult to separate from each other. Dispersive movements basically precede migratory ones, however, and the latter are increasingly dominated by movements in a particular direction.

The Kestrel's winter distribution extends north-east to a line approximating to permanent winter snow cover in Europe (Figure 2.2, page 20), and populations are increasingly migratory where winter conditions in their breeding range become harsher. Thus, tropical or subtropical races are mainly sedentary, populations in temperate areas are partially migratory and beyond this line they are migratory. In partially migratory populations, young birds are more migratory than adults and upland and northern elements more so than lowland.

As with other bird species, much of our knowledge of Kestrel movements derives from recoveries in the ringing schemes now run in most European countries. Ringing returns are subject to several important limitations, which influence the patterns recorded. Recoveries tend to be biased towards centres of population, dead Kestrels being more likely to be found near people than in Scottish deer forests, for example. Literacy contributes to this bias, for people in developed countries are more likely to know what a ring is and how to return it than are African tribesmen.

Recoveries in Europe may also be unduly biased towards areas where persecution is an important cause of mortality, and, in Britain, ringing effort may not be uniform in different regions and certainly is not in different age-groups of the population. Nevertheless, it is easy to over-estimate the significance of such limitations. A ringing recovery is an unequivocal fact. An area involved in a number of winter recoveries of Kestrels, for example, may not be the primary wintering area, but it is undeniable that Kestrels winter there.

Dispersal

Here, dispersal concerns the movements of young Kestrels after they first become independent, which varies from about a fortnight to a month after starting to leave the nest. My impression (untested) has been that juveniles disperse more quickly in my Welsh area than they did in Sussex farmland, perhaps because they quickly move out to open hill areas to take advantage of the abundant supply of large insects there, mainly dor beetles in August.

Older literature often suggests that adults drive their offspring away once the latter become independent but I have not found this to be so, although they were highly intolerant of neighbouring young in Sussex. Village (1990) suggested that young start to wander once no longer held by parental feeding, and this seems much more likely. I also noted that parents were not above poaching from their offspring or shouldering them away from a preferred hunting area, which possibly accelerates the process.

Dispersive movements feature mainly in July and August, and in Britain, of 644 records since 1950 of Kestrels ringed as nestlings and recovered in July/August in their first year, only thirteen made movements of more than 250 km and only one made a sea-crossing, from Shropshire to Ulster. The direction showed no dominant pattern. Thus, dispersive movements here are usually quite short and generally avoid sea-crossings.

Migrating Kestrels tend to move singly or in small groups rather than in soaring flocks; deserts are not barriers.

A similar picture has been recorded in European populations (e.g., Cavé 1968; Nielsen 1983). An interesting difference between Dutch and British Kestrels is that Dutch birds occur in their first July/August in Britain, mainly in eastern England, movements which involve a substantial sea-crossing. Such recoveries comprise 9 per cent of all the foreign-ringed Kestrels found in Britain up to the end of 1990, suggesting that it is a fairly regular pattern.

Further south, Swiss Kestrels behave rather differently, with a pronounced tendency to disperse west and north-west, followed by a marked south-west orientation during autumn migration proper. This west to north-west dispersal involves movements of up to 400 km and perhaps represents a move out into the nearest major lowland area (Cramp and Simmons 1979).

As with all bird movements, exceptional ones also occur at this period, and there is one record of a Kestrel nestling ringed in Luxembourg in June 1983 and recovered in Co. Clare, Eire, that August.

The general pattern of migration

The broad trend of Kestrel migration in Europe is north-east to south-west. This has been shown, for example, by studies of ringed Kestrels in Finland, Denmark, the Netherlands and Switzerland and of spring movements at Cape Bon, Tunisia (C.J. Mead, in Cramp and Simmons 1979); Swedish birds perform what is known as a 'leapfrog' migration, with those breeding furthest north (which are wholly migratory) wintering furthest south, in Africa. In fact, most Palearctic Kestrels wintering in trans-Saharan Africa are probably drawn from the fully migratory populations of north-east and eastern Europe and Russia. Although most Kestrels from more temperate European areas stay north of the Sahara (mostly within Europe), some certainly also cross it, and there are single recoveries from the Netherlands in Mauritania, Switzerland in Liberia, Czechoslovakia in Ghana and Germany in Nigeria (Moreau 1972). These very long-distance movements continue the south-west trend visible in the longer movements recorded in Europe generally. Cavé (1968) suggested that the south-west trend in Dutch Kestrels was misleading, being overemphasized by persecution in neighbouring areas of Belgium and France, where a high proportion of birds shot or killed inflated the number of recoveries. He separated these from recoveries resulting from other causes, but his figures still show a marked south-west orientation for birds in the latter category making movements of more than 200 km.

The pattern of recoveries described in Cramp and Simmons suggests that France, the Iberian Peninsula and, to a lesser extent, Italy and North Africa are significant wintering grounds for Kestrels from further north-east in Europe. The actual proportion cannot be estimated, and recoveries of Finnish birds from the Balkans and central Europe and of Danish birds from Austria and central Germany show the wintering range, at least, to be wider. A high proportion of migrant Kestrels from some areas are first-winter birds. Thus, in the Netherlands, Cavé found that his breeding adults showed a much greater tendency to winter nearby than did first-winter birds, and

BTO ringing records show a similar pattern for Britain. Further north-east the pattern changes: Danish results show an equal tendency among adults and first-winter individuals for long-distance movements (Nielsen 1983).

Like all falcons, Kestrels use active flapping flight on migration. They are known to make fairly long sea-crossings (regularly crossing the North Sea, for example) and to overfly the Sahara. Their movements occur on a broad front and, unlike soaring raptors, spectacular concentrations have not been recorded at major raptor-watching points such as Falsterbo in Sweden, Gibraltar, Malta, the Bosporus, or Eilat at the northern end of the Red Sea, seasonal totals of a few hundreds being typical. Radar studies at Gibraltar have shown that visual counts at such sites may underestimate true passage numbers because many birds pass overhead too high to be seen (Evans and Lathbury 1973). Nevertheless, the counts do show a broad uniformity in scale and little convincing sign of a preferred route, suggesting a widely dispersed movement. This seems to apply in spring and autumn.

At both seasons the period of movement is protracted. Spring passage is recorded through February to May, with a peak in March, at Gibraltar (Cortés *et al.* 1980); from mid February to mid June, with a peak in mid March to mid May at Malta (Beaman and Galea 1974); and from early February to mid June with a peak from mid March to mid April at Eilat (Shirihai and Christie 1992). Many Kestrels ringed in spring at Cape Bon (282 km west of Malta) have been recovered in summer from Archangel to the Caucasus and in west Siberia (C.J. Mead, in Cramp and Simmons 1979). The timing of arrivals through Russia and Siberia given by Dementiev and Gladkov (1951) also ties in well with the peaks noted at Malta and further east, and the latter relate quite well to departure from African winter quarters, where most have left areas south of the Sahara by the end of March (Brown, Urban and Newman 1982). Movements through Gibraltar, where the spring peak is earlier, possibly derive mainly from north-west European populations, where arrival on breeding grounds is earlier (page 76).

Autumn passage starts in late August in northern Europe and lasts until early November, but through much of Europe, including eastern Europe, the main passage period is September and into October. As one moves south the peak passage period is later, between mid September and mid October at the Col de Bretolet, on the Swiss-French border (Thiollay 1966), but October at Gibraltar. Birds begin to reappear in African winter quarters from late September. Rather little is known about movements of more eastern populations, but Siberian Kestrels certainly winter in India, for example (Dementiev and Gladkov).

Movements of British Kestrels

Over 30,000 British Kestrels have been ringed and over 3000 recovered. Here, I have concentrated on recoveries showing movements of 250 km or more or outside Britain, together with recoveries of continental birds in Britain. Any Kestrel moving 250 km within Britain is almost bound to find itself in a region of different basic characteristics, moving from uplands to lowlands, or from areas dominated by grassland farming to one dominated by tillage, and so on. Dispersive movements of British Kestrels in July and August (see above) also suggest strongly that crossing a substantial water barrier requires a stronger urge than mere dispersive wanderings. These longer movements, therefore, may outline fairly sharply the migratory behaviour of British Kestrels.

Such migrants comprise a limited proportion of the population. Altogether, there are 455 of these records for British-ringed birds and 81 of continental birds recovered in Britain, totalling about 16 per cent of all recoveries. Clearly, therefore, most British Kestrels make comparatively short movements within Britain.

The age structure of the British birds making longer movements deriving from all regions is dominated by first-winter individuals both in winter and during the main passage seasons (Table 9.1). Altogether, 88 per cent of total recoveries of Kestrels were ringed as nestlings or juveniles/first-years, and 11 per cent of these were involved in the movements summarized in Table 9.1 compared with only 3 per cent of older birds ringed. Cavé (1968) suggested that even this sort of calculation was distorted by the effects of persecution, as more young birds, being less wary, were shot. Such a pattern is not, however, evident in the recoveries of British birds.

It is much more difficult to estimate whether these young Kestrels continue to make such movements in subsequent years, as hardly any were handled more than once. In his Scottish area, however, Village observed no cases where birds leaving to winter elsewhere or wintering on

Table 9.1 *The age structure of British Kestrels recovered making movements of 250 km or more, or overseas, to winter or during passage (September to April).*

Area	Total recovered	Recovered in First Winter	Recovered in Second Winter	Recovered in Third Winter	Recovered in Fourth Winter	Recovered in Fifth Winter	Recovered Later
Scotland North							
Nestling or juvenile	51	48	2*			1	
Older	nil						
Scotland South							
Nestling or juvenile	90	68	15	4	1	1	
Older	6		2		2		2
England North							
Nestling or juvenile	155	123	20	5	2	1	4
Older	3		3				
England East							
Nestling or juvenile	58	48	5	3			2
Older	2		2				
England West and Wales							
Nestling or juvenile	28	23	3	1		1	
Older	nil						

* one bird was recovered in the same place in both its second and third winters, and may have settled there
Birds for which age was not clearly determined are omitted as are birds ringed at Bird Observatorys.
Source BTO ringing records 1909–91. Regions as in Figure 3.1.

site subsequently changed that habit, implying that it was fixed. Bearing in mind that mortality drops sharply after the first year and that 90 per cent of all the recoveries analysed here were of dead or disabled birds, the proportion of recoveries obtained from later years from the group of nestlings in Table 9.1 seems to me to support this. Presumably, the advantages of returning to a satisfactory wintering site, once found, outweigh any risks involved in migration. Northern Scottish birds appear to differ, however, apparently rarely making long or overseas movements after their first year. This region differs from all others in this respect, although the pattern does not vary between the other regions. The sex structure in these recoveries is also uneven: only 75 were sexed, but 54 (72 per cent) were females. Some of these were sexed as nestlings, but the same pattern applied with older birds and is confirmed in detailed studies.

The winter range of these British migrants is summarized in Table 9.2. Winter is here defined as November to January inclusive, when Kestrels seem to be fairly static and are probably on their true wintering station. Although most of these birds were found in southern Britain and France, the movements from northern Scotland were orientated distinctly more south-eastwards and 73 per cent of the winter recoveries in the Netherlands and Germany derive from the region. Probably because of the longer sea-crossing this involves, these birds also travel furthest to winter, with a median distance of 787 km in the movements considered here, compared with 350–450 km for the other regions. As noted in all studies of British Kestrels, southern birds are found more often in Europe simply because they are closer. The broad pattern suggested by these records is a general southerly shift for winter by a proportion of the British population, particularly of young birds.

As yet we do not have an analysis of regional ringing effort, so we cannot easily say what proportion of Kestrels from each region are involved in these movements. The number recovered depends largely on ringing effort. Detailed studies by Snow (1968) and Village (1990), however,

Table 9.2 *The winter distribution of migrant Kestrels ringed in Britain 1909–90.*

NUMBER OF RECOVERIES

	Belgium	Britain	France	Germany	Iberia	Ireland	The Netherlands	Sweden
Scotland North	0	17	6	3	0	0	5	0
Scotland South	1	40	11	0	1	4	1	0
England North	1	44	27	1	3	3	1	1
England East	2	8	16	0	4	0	0	0
England West and Wales	0	3	10	0	2	0	0	0
Total	4	112	70	4	10	7	7	1

Note: the French recoveries include three from the Channel Isles.
For definitions see text. Regions as in Figure 3.1.

Figure 9.1 *Distribution of migrant British Kestrels (moving 250 km or more or overseas) wintering in Britain and Ireland.*

KEY
- ☐ 1–2 records
- ☐ 3–4 "
- ☐ 5–7 "
- ■ 8+ "

Source BTO ringing records 1909–91

have shown that northern Kestrels are broadly more migratory than southern ones. This may need qualifying in two respects, one being that very few northern Scottish birds seem to move far after their first winter; the second is that Kestrels from Wales and south-west England are probably more migratory than the records in Table 9.1 suggest. This probability is suggested by comparing the Winter Atlas (Lack 1986) and the New Breeding Atlas (Gibbons *et al.* in press). This shows that, in western England and Wales, 51 per cent of the 10-km squares occupied by Kestrels in winter held only one or two individuals but, in the breeding season, the proportion with the lowest numerical category was only 25 per cent, indicating considerable infilling; the total number of occupied squares did not differ significantly. This does not occur in eastern England, where the figures were 12 and 8 per cent, respectively. This is not just a question of there being more high ground in the west, as the pattern was widely dispersed irrespective of altitude. Nor is the west a region of severe winter climate: in upland north Breconshire, for example, snow rarely lies for long below 300–450 m. Rather, the climate is wet, and it may be this which induces inexperienced young Kestrels in particular to winter elsewhere.

Figures 9.1 and 9.2 illustrate the winter distribution of these longer movements in Britain and France, respectively. They have one marked feature in common. The main concentrations of records in both countries fall in areas dominated by arable farming (71 per cent of farmland in France and 80 per cent in England) and, in both, improved farmland is the primary land use in these districts, comprising 75 per cent or more of land area. Such a habitat preference may also explain the behaviour of northern Scottish Kestrels, where second-winter and adult birds moving off high ground possibly do no more than shift to winter in the major area of arable farmland concentrated in Aberdeen and neighbouring parts of Grampian. There is also a noticeable lack of long-distance recoveries from the intensive arable areas of East Anglia and Lincolnshire. Without details of ringing effort this is difficult to evaluate, but only one of 46 ringing recoveries Village obtained from farmland areas (Rutland and Huntingdon) qualifies for inclusion in this analysis and only four others he ringed there moved more than 80 km, suggesting a very sedentary habit. All these major areas of arable farmland are also characterized by a relatively dry climate.

Continental Kestrels also winter in Britain, where recoveries have been obtained during November to January of birds ringed in Sweden (one), Norway (two), Denmark (three), Poland (one), Germany (one), the Netherlands (nine) and Belgium (one), while recoveries in September, October and February extend that range to Finland, Czechoslovakia and France. Nearly all these Kestrels have been found in lowland farmland from Aberdeen south, but there seems to be a less marked concentration

Figure 9.2 *Distribution of British-ringed Kestrels wintering in France.*

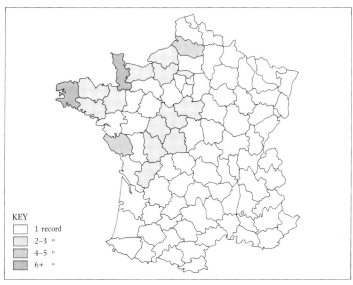

KEY
☐ 1 record
▨ 2–3 "
▧ 4–5 "
▨ 6+ "

Source BTO ringing records 1909–91.

in the eastern counties than is the case with British birds and there are nine recoveries from Wales, south-west England and Ireland.

Comparing the winter distribution of these recoveries with that of the main passage seasons shows few major differences, although there is a recovery in Morocco in February of a Kestrel ringed in Grampian. Many found during passage seasons may have been wintering, but one cannot be sure. Spring recoveries of continental Kestrels in Britain show why. In March and April these are concentrated in east-coast counties, in marked contrast to the winter birds, and there is none from Scandinavia recovered during February to April, tying in neatly with Nielsen's observation (1983) that migrants return to Denmark from February on – perhaps too neatly, for Scandinavian Kestrels have been found in Britain in summer (see below).

The structure of the winter population

Because females and young birds appear to be more migratory than males or adults, there should be an imbalance in the wintering populations in some areas and this does seem to be so. Village (1990) found that in his Scottish area adult males predominated in winter, and the disparity was more marked in a poor vole year. Similarly, in six winters in Wales, I have consistently found more adult males staying in my study area than individuals I have identified as females and, in all but two winters when numbers were equal, more adult males than any brown-tailed birds; in Sussex, however, there appeared to be no significant differences in two winters on 40 km² of mixed and arable farmland. Working with marked Kestrels in his farmland areas, Village found more brown-tailed birds than adult males in winter, but there were more adult males than adult females and many more first-year males than first-year females. Similar observations have been made in France, where Yeatman-Berthelot (1991) noted a predominance of adult males wintering in the north-east but not in the west and south. Village also found a greater preponderance of females in arable than in mixed farmland and suggested that this might have arisen from a habitat preference. As the sexes tend to hunt in different habitats (page 61), this seems likely. Broadly, therefore, adult males tend to remain in more climatically rigorous areas (which, for Kestrels, may include wet climates) for the winter and females and young birds tend to move. This perhaps arises because holding on to a good breeding territory is more important to breeding males than to females, which may have a greater influence in mate selection (page 80).

Interchange between breeding populations

There is clearly considerable interchange of populations between Britain and continental Europe in winter. There are also 26 records of British Kestrels recovered in the breeding season (May to early August) either overseas or more than 250 km from the ringing site and ten of continental birds found in Britain in the same season, although three of these latter were ringed at seasons suggesting that they were in fact British birds trapped in winter quarters. All the British birds were ringed as nestlings, except one as full grown, and are excluded from Table 9.1.

These recoveries overlap the wintering range, with British Kestrels found in Europe from Norway around to Ireland (with an exceptional one in Morocco) and European birds found in Britain and deriving from Finland to Belgium. Kestrels from Scotland and northern England have also been found widely scattered across eastern and western England and Wales. There is, of course, no proof that these individuals were breeding where found (all but one were found dead or disabled), but the age composition of these recoveries differs sharply from that of wintering or passage birds in Table 9.1, 50 per cent being recovered in the second summer or later after birth as against 19 per cent. This suggests strongly to me that the birds had indeed settled in the areas where found, rather than being lingering migrants, when a higher proportion of young birds might have been expected. A fairly regular interchange between breeding populations in north-west Europe therefore seems likely.

Mortality

Ringing recoveries can also tell us something of how long Kestrels live and why they die. Estimating mortality from ringing returns is subject to a number of potential biases, one of the most intractable of which, for raptors, may be variations in the impact of persecution on different populations or age groups (see Newton 1979 for a detailed discussion). The causes of death most often recorded in ringing returns may also be less important with the population, because, for example, recoveries themselves tend to biased towards areas with people and therefore hazards such as traffic. As a general rule such hazards do not alter the frequency of death, but only its causes.

Nevertheless, these studies provide some idea of what happens. Using ringing returns, Snow (1968) estimated that about 40 per cent of Kestrels survived their first year and 53 per cent of those the second, with a combined survival of 66 per cent for later years. Village's (1990) figures for a similar exercise were 32 per cent, 66 per cent and 69 per cent, respectively. The discrepancies arose mainly from differences in the points at which the year was changed, which affected the number of deaths assigned to the first year especially. The main result from these analyses is that many more young birds die than do adults, a trend that is general among all bird species. The same trend has been shown in European studies, although the actual rates recorded vary, again perhaps largely because of differences in methods. The seasonal pattern of mortality varies somewhat. Newton *et al.* (1982) found a peak in August, when young were newly independent, and a low in May–June during breeding, but otherwise the overall pattern was fairly uniform; they also found no bias towards either sex in the birds they examined. Both Village (1990) and Cavé (1968) found that young from early broods were less vulnerable than those from late ones. Brown (1976) thought that calculations based on ringing overestimated mortality because he could not relate adult survival

119

and productivity. He estimated, however, that only 11 per cent of Kestrels survived into their third year, but Snow showed this to be 21 per cent. Many adults are not recruited into the breeding population until approaching their third year (page 80).

What kills Kestrels? We have two sources of information: ringing returns and the study by Newton *et al.* (1982). Ringing returns include the recovery circumstances of each bird, but by far the largest category is 'found dead'. They can give some idea of the sorts of accidents Kestrels meet but little of their relative importance, and they greatly underestimate factors such as disease and starvation. Newton *et al.*'s study was based on the post-mortem examination of carcases sent in to Monks Wood Experimental Station. It gives a much clearer idea of the significance of starvation and disease: 29 per cent of deaths were attributed to starvation and 11 per cent to disease. Only 4 per cent of Kestrels were found shot, and the other main causes of death noted were collisions and accidents (23 per cent), unknown (20 per cent) and haemorrhage (13 per cent). Starvation occurred most often among young birds and particularly during July to October (41 per cent of records). With young Kestrels, survival is clearly a matter of finding a good area to settle and learning to exploit it; many fail. Whether or not the level of starvation found was truly representative of what happens, the indication that it may be the most important single factor in mortality seems convincing.

I have not examined the complete ringing records, but it is interesting to compare causes of death in long-distance migrants in Britain with those in neighbouring countries of Europe. The main differences are that traffic casualties were commoner in Britain and persecution commoner in Europe, neither perhaps unexpected. Both Glue (1971) and Newton *et al.* (1982) observed an increase in traffic casualties among British Kestrels. The latter often hunt along road verges, but this trend may reflect not just increasing traffic density but also changes in the hunting habitat now available in some farmland areas, where road verges may be an increasingly important component. A surprising number of Kestrels drown, often in cattle troughs, and 10 per cent or more of those found dead were in buildings, having perhaps died at roost.

No study seems to have detected a clear trend in the number of Kestrels found dead over the period since 1945, which seems odd in view of the probable impact of pesticides in the late 1950s and early 1960s (page 35). Newton *et al.*, however, noted that their records were not truly representative of what happens to the whole population, being biased towards mortality associated with human activities. They did observe, however, that haemorrhage as a cause of death was associated with high concentrations of organochlorines in the liver, and that the proportion of Kestrels dying from haemorrhage declined from 26 per cent in 1971–75 to 9 per cent in 1976–79, when these chemicals were being withdrawn from use. Thus, the importance of organochlorines as a cause of death seems clear.

Another reason why trends are not apparent in the ringing returns is possibly that these are severely biased towards Kestrels ringed as nestlings (90 per cent of records). If pesticides bore particularly on breeding adults, the ringing returns might be muted because little was done. Village also pointed out that the impact of persecution in Britain was declining when that of pesticides was increasing, which would have masked trends from particular causes.

It is not clear how important the killing by Man of mainly young Kestrels in their first autumn/winter is in conservation terms. It seems unlikely, however, to have much overall effect, for, when so many die anyway, very large numbers would have to be killed to influence populations. It is the selective persecution of breeding adults that most affects populations. The Kestrel has survived as a common feature of our countryside because it is highly adaptable to and tolerant of Man's activities. With a modicum of consideration and thought, I see no reason why this should not always be so.

Select
Bibliography

Adair, P., *Ann. Scot. Nat. Hist. Soc.*, 6 (1891), 219–31

Ash, J.S., *British Birds*, 53 (1960), 285–300 *ibid.*, 58 (1965), 469–70

Balfour, E., *Bird Notes*, 26 (1955), 245–53

Bannerman, D.A., and W.M., *Birds of the Atlantic Islands, vol. 4*, Oliver and Boyd, Edinburgh, 1968.

Beaman, M., and Galea, C., *Ibis*, 116 (1974), 419–31

Beukeboom, L., Dijkstra, C., Daan, S., and Meijer, T., *Ornis Scand.*, 19 (1988), 41–8

Bijleveld, M., *Birds of Prey in Europe*, Macmillan, London, 1974

Borrer, W., *Sussex Birds*, London, 1891

Bradley, D.E., *British Birds*, 59 (1966), 192

Brown, L.H., *African Birds of Prey*, Collins, London, 1970
British Birds of Prey, London, 1976

Brown, L.H., and Amadon, D., *Eagles, Hawks and Falcons of the World*, Country Life, London, 1968

Brown, L.H., Urban, E.K., and Newman, K., *The Birds of Africa, vol. 1*, Academic Press, London, 1982

Buckland, S.T., Bell, M.V., and Picozzi, N., *The Birds of North-east Scotland*, North-east Scotland Bird Club, 1990

Cadbury, C.J., *Death by Design*, RSPB/NCC Report, 1991

Cade, T.J., *The Falcons of the World*, Collins, London, 1982

Cavé, A.J., *Netherlands Journal of Zoology*, 18(3) (1968), 313–407

Chancellor, R.D. (ed.), *World Conference on Birds of Prey*, ICBP, Cambridge, 1977 [accounts of status by the following were consulted: Bécsy, L., and Keve, A. (Hungary); Dyck, J., Eskildsen, J., and Møller, H.S. (Denmark); Garzon, J. (Spain); Kesteloot, E.J.J. (Belgium); Massa, B. (Sicily); Puscariu, V., and Filipascu, A. (Romania); Segnestam, M., and Helander, B (Sweden); Sládek, J. (Czechoslovakia); Sultana, J., and Gauci, C. (Malta); and Terrasse, J-F. (France)]

Corbet, G.B., and Southern, H.N., *The Handbook of British Mammals*, Blackwell, Oxford, 1977

Cortés, J.E., Finlayson, J.C., Mosquera, M.A., and Garcia, E.F.J., *The Birds of Gibraltar*, Gibraltar Bookshop, 1980

Cramp, S., and Simmons, K.E.L. (eds.), *The Birds of the Western Palearctic, vol. 2*, OUP, Oxford, 1979

Dare, P.J., *Naturalist*, 111 (1986), 49–54

Dare, P.J., and Hamilton, L.I., *Devon Birds*, 21 (1968), 22–31

Davis, T.A.W., *Bird Study*, 22 (1975), 85–91

Dementiev, G.P., and Gladkov, N.A. (eds.), *Birds of the Soviet Union, vol. 1*, Moscow State Publishing House, Moscow, 1951

Dijkstra, C., Daan, S., and Buker, J.B., *Functional Ecology*, 4 (1990), 143–7

Easy, G.M.S., *Cambridge Bird Report, 1989* (1990), 59–63

Ellis, J.C.S., *British Birds*, 39 (1946), 113–15

Evans, P.R., and Lathbury, G.W., *Ibis*, 115 (1973), 572–85

Fairley, J.S., *Irish Naturalist*, 17 (1973), 407–9

Fairley, J.S., and McLean, A., *British Birds*, 58 (1965), 145–8

Fennell, C.M., *Condor*, 56 (1954), 106–7

Ferguson-Lees, I.J., *British Birds*, 65 (1972), 257–8

Forrest, H.E., *The Fauna of North Wales*, London, 1907

Génsbøl, B., *Birds of Prey of Britain and Europe*, Collins, London, 1989

Gibbons, D.W., Reid, J.B., and Chapman, R.A., *The New Atlas of Breeding Birds in Britain and Ireland: 1988–1991*, T. and A.D. Poyser, London, in press

Gladstone, H.S., *The Birds of Dumfries*, Witherby, London, 1910

Glue, D.E., *Bird Study*, 18 (1971), 137–46

Grigg, D., *English Agriculture: an historical perspective*, Blackwell, Oxford, 1989

Haines, C.R., *Notes on the Birds of Rutland*, London, 1907

Hasenclever, H., Kostrzewa, A., and Kostrzewa, R., *J. Orn.*, 130 (1989), 229–37

Hughes, S.W.M., and Dougharty, F.W., *Sussex Bird Report*, 31 (1979), 78–80

Hutchinson, C.D., *Birds in Ireland*, T. and A.D. Poyser, Calton, 1989

ICBP, *Working Conference on Birds of Prey and Owls*, Cambridge, 1964 [accounts of status by the following were consulted: Kesteloot, E., and Wille, H. (Belgium); Przygodda, W. (rodenticides and birds of prey); Rooth, J., and Bruijns, M.F.M. (The Netherlands); and Terrasse, J-F. (France)]

Itämies, J., and Korpimäki, E., *Aquilo Ser. Zool.*, 25 (1987), 21–31

Joyce, B., Williams, G., and Woods, A., *RSPB Conservation Review*, 2 (1988), 34–7

Korpimäki, E. [1985a], *Ann. Zool. Fennici*, 22 (1985), 91–104
[1985b], *Ornis Fennica*, 62 (1985), 130–7
Ibid., 63 (1986), 84–90

Kostrzewa, A., and Kostrzewa, R., *Ibis*, 132 (1990), 550–9

Lack, D., *Birds of Cambridgeshire*, Cambridge, 1934

Lack, P., *Atlas of Wintering Birds in Britain and Ireland*, T. and A.D. Poyser, Calton, 1986

Lilford, Lord, *The Birds of Northamptonshire*, London, 1895

Lovari, S., *Raptor Research*, 8(3/4) (1974), 45–57

Marchant, J.H., Hudson, R., Carter, S.P., and Whittington, P., *Population trends in British Breeding Birds*, BTO, Thetford, 1990

Masman, D., Daan, S., and Dijkstra, C., *Journal of Animal Ecology*, 57 (1988), 411–32

Mather, J., *The Birds of Yorkshire*, Croom Helm, London, 1986

Mead, C.J., and Pepler, G.R.M., *British Birds*, 68 (1975), 89–99

Meijer, T., Daan, S., and Dijkstra, C., *Ardea*, 76 (1988), 141–54

Mikkola, H., *Owls of Europe*, T. and A.D. Poyser, Calton, 1983

Montier, D., *London Bird Report*, 32 (1968), 81–92
The Atlas of Breeding Birds of the London Area, Batsford, London, 1977

Moreau, R.E., *The Palearctic-African Bird Migration Systems*, Academic Press, London, 1972

Murton, R., *Man and Birds*, Collins, London, 1971

Newton, A., *A Dictionary of Birds*, A. & C. Black, London, 1896

Newton, I., *Journal of Applied Ecology*, 11 (1974), 95–101
Population Ecology of Raptors, T. and A.D. Poyser, Calton, 1979
BTO News, 131 (1984), 6–7
The Sparrowhawk, T. and A.D. Poyser, Calton, 1986

Newton, I., Bell, A.A., and Wyllie, I., *British Birds*, 75 (1982), 195–204

Newton, I., and Chancellor, R.D. (eds.), *Conservation Studies on Raptors*, 1985 [accounts of status by the following were consulted: Halmann, B. (Greece); Muntaner, J., and CRPR (Catalonia); and Palma, L. (Portugal)]

Newton, I., and Haas, M.B., *British Birds*, 77 (1984), 47–70

Newton, I., Wyllie, I., and Asher, A., *Ibis*, 133 (1991), 162–9

Nielsen, B.P., *Dansk Orn. Foren. Tidsskr.*, 77 (1983), 1–12

Noré, T., *Alauda*, 47 (1979), 259–69

Oakes, C., *The Birds of Lancashire*, Oliver and Boyd, Edinburgh, 1953

Orwin, C.S., and Whetham, E.H., *History of British Agriculture, 1846–1914*, Longmans, Green and Co., London, 1964

O'Connor, R.J., and Shrubb, M., *Farming and Birds*, CUP, Cambridge, 1986

Parr, D., *Surrey Bird Report 1967* (1969), 35–42

Parslow, J.L.F., *Breeding Birds of Britain and Ireland*, T. and A.D. Poyser, Berkhamsted, 1969

Pettifor, R.A., *British Birds*, 76 (1983), 206–14

Picozzi, N., and Hewson, R., *Scottish Birds*, 6 (1970), 185–91

Poore, M.E.D., see Woodell, S.J.R. (ed.)

Prestt, I., *Bird Study*, 12 (1965), 196–221

Ratcliffe, D.A., *The Peregrine Falcon*, T. and A.D. Poyser, Calton, 1980
Bird-life of Upland and Mountain, CUP, Cambridge, 1990

Raptor Group RUG/RIJP, *Mammal Rev.*, 12 (1982), 169–81

Riddle, G.S., *Scottish Birds*, 10 (1979), 201–16
Scottish Birds, 14 (1987), 138–45

Rijnsdorp, A., Daan, S., and Dijkstra, C., *Oecologia*, 50 (1981), 391–406

Roberts, E.L., *British Birds*, 39 (1946), 217–18

Salim Ali and Ripley, S.D., *Handbook of the Birds of India and Pakistan*, 2nd ed. vol. 1, OUP, Oxford, 1978

Sharrock, J.T.R. (ed.), *The Atlas of Breeeding Birds in Britain and Ireland*, T. and A.D. Poyser, Berkhamsted, 1976

Shawyer, C.R., *The Barn Owl in the British Isles: its past, present and future*, The Hawk Trust, London, 1987

Shirihai, H., and Christie, D.A., *British Birds*, 85 (1992), 141–86

Shrubb, M., *Bird Study*, 17 (1970), 1–15
Ibid., 27 (1980), 109–15
Ibid., 29 (1982), 121-8
Ibid., 40 (1993), 63–73

Simms, C., *Bird Study*, 8 (1961), 148–51
British Birds, 70 (1977), 499–500

Snow, D.W., *Bird Study*, 15 (1968) 65–83

Stevenson, H., *Birds of Norfolk*, London, 1866

Taylor, K., Hudson, R., and Horne, G., *Bird Study*, 35 (1988), 109–18

Thiollay, J-M., *Nos Oiseaux*, 27 (1963), 71–3
Ibid., 28 (1966), 229–51

[1968a], *L'Oiseaux*, 38 (1968), 187–208
[1968b], *Nos Oiseaux*, 29 (1968), 251–69

Thomson, A.L. (ed.), *A New Dictionary of Birds*, Nelson, London, 1964

Ticehurst, C.B., *The Birds of Suffolk*, Gurney and Jackson, London, 1932

Van den Brink, F.H., *Field Guide to the Mammals of Britain and Europe*, Collins, London, 1967

Vaurie, C., *The Birds of the Palaearctic Fauna, vol. 1.*, Witherby, London, 1965

Village, A. [1983a], *Ardea*, 71 (1983), 117–24
[1983b], *J. Anim. Ecol.*, 52 (1983), 635–45
The Kestrel, T. and A.D. Poyser, London, 1990

Village, A., Marquiss, M., and Cook, D.C., *Ringing and Migration*, 3 (1980), 53–9

Voous, K.H., *The Atlas of European Birds*, Nelson, London, 1960

Walpole-Bond, J., *A History of Sussex Birds*, Witherby, London, 1938

Watson, A., *Birds* (Autumn 1991) 19–24

Witherby, H.F., Jourdain, F.C.R., Ticehurst, N.F., and Tucker, B.W., *The Handbook of British Birds*, Witherby, London, 1952

Woodell, S.J.R. (ed.), *The English Landscape, Past, Present and Future*, OUP, Oxford, 1985

Yalden, D.W., *The Identification of Remains in Owl Pellets*, Mammal Society, Reading, 1977
Bird Study, 27 (1980), 235–8

Yalden, D.W., and Warburton, A.B., *Bird Study*, 26 (1979), 163–70

Yeatman-Berthelot, D., *Atlas des Oiseaux de France en Hiver*, Société Ornithologique de France, 1991

Scientific Names
of Species

BIRDS
Shelduck *Tadorna tadorna*
Red Kite *Milvus milvus*
Griffon Vulture *Gyps fulvus*
Marsh Harrier *Circus aeruginosus*
Hen Harrier *C. cyaneus*
Goshawk *Accipiter gentilis*
Sparrowhawk *A. nisus*
Buzzard *Buteo buteo*
Lesser Kestrel *Falco naumanni*
Greater Kestrel *F. rupicoloides*
Fox Kestrel *F. alopex*
American Kestrel *F. sparverius*
Common Kestrel *Falco tinnunculus*
Madagascar Kestrel *F. newtoni*
Mauritius Kestrel *F. punctatus*
Seychelles Kestrel *F. araea*
Moluccan Kestrel *F. moluccensis*
Australian Kestrel *F. cenchroides*
Grey Kestrel *F. ardosiaceus*
Dickinson's Kestrel *F. dickinsoni*
Barred or Banded Kestrel *F. zoniventris*
Red-footed Falcon *F. vespertinus*
Eastern Red-footed Falcon *F. amurensis*
Merlin *F. columbarius*
Hobby *F. subbuteo*
Eleonora's Falcon *F. eleonorae*
Sooty Falcon *F. concolor*
Laggar Falcon *F. jugger*
Gyrfalcon *F. rusticolus*
Peregrine *F. peregrinus*
Grey Partridge *Perdix perdix*
Pheasant *Phasianus colchicus*
Moorhen *Gallinula chloropus*
Lapwing *Vanellus vanellus*
Black-headed Gull *Larus ridibundus*
Great Black-backed Gull *L. marinus*
Stock Dove *Columba oenas*
Woodpigeon *C. palumbus*
Collared Dove *Streptopelia decaocto*
Barn Owl *Tyto alba*
Eagle Owl *Bubo bubo*
Little Owl *Athene noctua*
Tawny Owl *Strix aluco*
Short-eared Owl *Asio flammeus*
Nightjar *Caprimulgus europaeus*
Roller *Coracias garrulus*
Skylark *Alauda arvensis*

Sand Martin *Riparia riparia*
Swallow *Hirundo rustica*
Meadow Pipit *Anthus pratensis*
Black Redstart *Phoenicurus ochruros*
Blackbird *Turdus merula*
Redwing *T. iliacus*
Magpie *Pica pica*
Jackdaw *Corvus monedula*
Rook *C. frugilegus*
Carrion Crow *C. corone*
Raven *C. corax*
Starling *Sturnus vulgaris*
sparrows *Passer spp.*
Yellowhammer *Emberiza citrinella*

MAMMALS
Hedgehog *Erinaceus europaeus*
Mole *Talpa europaea*
Common Shrew *Sorex araneus*
Pigmy Shrew *S. minutus*
Rabbit *Oryctolagus cuniculus*
Hare *Lepus capensis*
Red Squirrel *Sciurus vulgaris*
Grey Squirrel *S. carolinensis*
Bank Vole *Clethrionomys glareolus*
Short-tailed Vole *Microtus agrestis*
Common Vole *M. arvalis*
Wood Mouse *Apodemus sylvaticus*
Harvest Mouse *Micromys minutus*
House Mouse *Mus musculus*
rats *Rattus spp.*
Weasel *Mustela nivalis*

REPTILES
Slow-worm *Anguis fragilis*
Common Lizard *Lacerta vivipara*

INVERTEBRATES
dragonflies *Zygoptera, Anisoptera*
earwigs *Dermaptera*
grasshoppers, crickets *Orthoptera*
butterflies, moths *Lepidoptera*
craneflies *Tipulidae*
ants *Hymenoptera*
beetles *Coleoptera*
ground beetles *carabidae*
dor beetles *geotrupes*
earthworms *Lumbricidae*

Index